Adopted

BECKY McGURRIN

CHRISTIAN LIGHT PUBLICATIONS

Harrisonburg, Virginia 22802

ADOPTED

Christian Light Publications, Inc.
Harrisonburg, Virginia 22802
© 2012 by Christian Light Publications, Inc.
Printed in the United States of America

Third Printing, 2014

Inside Photos: All photos supplied by the author.

Cover and inside design: David W. Miller
Cover Graphics: Evan McGurrin; Laura Rohrer;
David W. Miller; ©iStockphoto.com; Thinkstock

ISBN 978-0-87813-725-1

Dedication

For Pat.

And for the God

who loves her.

Pat is a real person.

Her story is true.

Conversations and minor details

have been supplied by the author

to make her story easier to tell.

a·dop′tion,
adopt.] the
being adopted;
treating of the child of anoth
b) the taking into fellows
as the adoptio

chapter 1

S he held the baby tightly in her arms, tears silently streaming down her face—tears not of joy, but of grief, and of loss, and of never going back. She caressed the baby's skin with her eyes as the priest gently brushed his fingers up and across its smooth, pink forehead. The child was so delicate, so quiet, so achingly beautiful.

"You have a lovely little girl there," said the priest.

Pat did not answer him. She knew her daughter was lovely, indescribably so. Hadn't she spent the last day and a half counting her toes, stroking her silky hair, and breathing in her sweet, powdery smell? The child was more than lovely; she was perfect—perfect enough to pass anyone's inspection.

All that was left was to see that she was christened with the name Pat had dreamed about for the last nine months—Suzzane.

The ceremony didn't take long. It was just a formality, really, a sprinkle of water on the hair, a smear of oil above the brow, and a few prayers. But Pat felt better about things now. Well, a little better anyway. At least her daughter would have a place in Heaven and a name given to her by her own mother. That would have to be enough.

The nurse handed Pat a Kleenex. She nodded, said a quick thanks, and dried her eyes.

She felt herself smiling as she was wheeled down the short hallway from the chapel to the nursery. Though she wouldn't have been able to explain why—even to herself. What did she need Vince for anyway? She was going to get a job and find a little place for her and little Harry to live, and they would be happy again. And Suzzane? She would never have to know what it is like to be hungry, or afraid, or betrayed. No, for her, it would be different—she was going to belong to a family.

Pat watched through the glass, as the nurse wrapped the pink blanket more snugly around Suzzane's tiny body and tenderly laid the sleeping child in the bassinet. Yes, her little girl was going to have a good family.

Pat went back to her room alone.

She climbed into the bed and cautiously laid her head against the pillow. The headache that had tormented her ever since she had walked down to the pay phone to call Vince was threatening to return. Vince, the wretch. She had loved him once—at least she had thought she did. He had seemed so affectionate and kind. Now he was a loathsome thing.

How could she have been so stupid? His kind of love wasn't real. It was self-centered and deceitful and only as big as what he could get out of it. What a miserable loser. He didn't deserve to be a father.

But she didn't really hate him; at least, not the way she wished she could. No, she felt more pity for him than hate. He was a selfish user who didn't know what real love was, and she was lucky to be rid of him.

Sleep had almost found her, when Pat heard the sound of soft shoes on linoleum that announced a visitor. The distinctive smell of Pall Mall cigarettes, lightly masked by Ivory soap, told her that it was her mother. Pat opened her eyes.

Ma was a tiny woman. Shoulder-length gray hair and deep lines on her forehead made her look much older than fifty-one. Life had been hard on her. Still, she looked nice in the yellow and orange dress that hung to just below her knees. It was her best dress—this visit was important to her.

"How are you doing?" Ma asked.

Pat sat up against the pillow. "I'm doing good. How did you get here?"

"What does that matter? I brought you these." Ma held out a brown paper bag. It looked new. She must have stopped at Woolworth's on the way to the hospital.

Pat peeked inside the bag, then pulled out a pair of soft, blue slippers. They looked just like the kind Ma wore herself. "They're pretty," Pat said. "Thanks, these floors are cold. Would you mind setting them on the nightstand for me?"

Ma placed the slippers neatly on the nightstand, then turned the green leather chair so that it faced the bed and sat down. Pat leaned her head back and closed her eyes. The headache was swelling again.

The two women sat quietly for several minutes, Pat in the bed and Ma in the chair. It was Ma who broke the silence. "Patsy, I can't believe you're going to give her up. I never saw such a beautiful baby."

"You saw her?" asked Pat, her eyes now wide open.

Ma looked puzzled. "Of course I saw her, just before I came in here."

"No one was supposed to see her. I told them that."

"You can see right through the window; she's the only white baby in the nursery. It wasn't hard to figure out which one was her."

"You shouldn't have even gone to the nursery. I told you on the phone I didn't want any visitors, and you knew I didn't want anyone to see her."

"That's ridiculous. Of course I can see my own granddaughter."

"Ma, you shouldn't think of her as your granddaughter; you're just making it harder on yourself."

"Bah! Of course she's my granddaughter. And I don't see how you can even think of giving her up!"

Pat took a deep breath. This was hard enough without her mother's interference. "You know how it is for Harry and me. We're barely making it. I can't possibly take care of another child. Not the way she deserves. I want her to grow up in a family—a good family—and to have a father who loves her and cares about her."

"Your father was never around, and you turned out fine."

"That's just it. I don't want my daughter to go through what I've gone through. Ma, I want her to have a family."

"Children belong with their mother," Ma retorted.

Pat closed her eyes again. She rubbed her temples and squeezed the back of her neck. They had warned her to lie flat after the spinal. Why didn't she ever listen to people who knew better?

"Does Vince know?" Ma asked.

"I called him yesterday," answered Pat. "Well, I called the dispatcher; Vince was out on a run. It wouldn't have made any difference. He dumped me the minute he found out I was expecting; he certainly wouldn't care that he had a daughter."

"He doesn't deserve a daughter."

"That's what the dispatcher said."

"You told him?"

"You bet I did! I wasn't gonna waste the call. He not only wrote down my message; he said he would post it on the bulletin board. All the other drivers read it before Vince even got back."

"What did it say?"

"The message? 'Congratulations, Vince—you have just become the father of a beautiful baby girl.'"

"You didn't! Serves him right—the deadbeat."

Ma left soon after that, but her words echoed in Pat's mind. *Children belong with their mother.* The words had shaken Pat's resolve. Would Suzzane really be better off with other parents? Harry seemed to be doing okay, and all he had was a mother. If love was all that was needed to raise a child,

Pat certainly had enough to shower on both of her children. And her desire to keep Suzzane, to cling to her forever, was almost more than she could bear. But love wasn't the issue. It was the other things. Pat knew, too well, what it was like to grow up on welfare, never knowing when your father would be around, and dreading that he would. No, she wasn't going to put Suzzane through that. "Pat Vohwinkel," she said out loud, as if making a vow that she would not dare to break, "your daughter deserves to grow up in a family, and you are not going to let your own desires get in the way of that."

To prevent herself from thinking about the decision any longer (and to silence Ma's words), she reached over to the TV controller and flipped it on. Perry Mason was on, one of her favorite shows. It was a rerun, of course, but that didn't matter. Perry's secretary, Della Street, was a character Pat adored, and she would watch any episode just to see how the smart, savvy, and gorgeous secretary always helped her boss solve his latest case.

Della would know how to get out of this mess, thought Pat. *I bet she could raise two kids, keep her house clean, and still earn enough money to eat out every night. I don't suppose I'll ever be anything more than a waitress.* Pat fell asleep somewhere in the second half of the show.

The sky was overcast and gray on Pat's last day at the hospital. And it was the final day, the last day she would see her daughter—forever. It was also the longest day of her life. The nurse had already discharged her and left the room. Pat dragged herself to the bathroom and stood before the mirror. She was normally a pretty woman, dark-haired, twenty-two, with a slight build inherited from her mother. Today, she looked drawn and thin.

This is it, she said, in a quiet, sad corner of her mind. *The day you ruin your life and give up the most precious thing you've ever been given. God help me to go through with it.*

She dressed quickly in the jumper she had worn when she came to the hospital four days before. It hung on her tiny shivering body like a threadbare, empty sack. *I guess I won't be needing this dress anymore.*

Evelyn Godwin, the social worker, knocked on the door as Pat stuffed her discharge papers into her tote bag. "Mrs. Vohwinkel?"

"Hi, come on in. I'm about finished here."

"I thought it might be easier for you to sign the final release papers here in your room, but we can make another trip to the nursery if you'd like. Nothing is permanent yet, you know."

"No, let's do it here. I said good-bye to Suzzane a little while ago."

"Are you one hundred percent sure you want to go through with the adoption?"

"Yes. It's the best thing for her. I'm sure of that."

"Okay then, there are just a few more forms for you to sign, and you'll be free to go."

Pat signed the papers with the determination that had formed weeks before, but had only solidified in the last few days. The signatures looked blurry, the way things look through a window lashed by rain. A tear dropped onto one of the pages. Pat tried to wipe it away.

"That's okay," said Mrs. Godwin. "Tears are very fitting when signing papers like these."

"Can I ask a question?" asked Pat, when the papers had been tucked out of sight in a portfolio. "You once said that Suzzane would be able to keep her first name, even after she was adopted. Is that still true?"

"Yes. The adopting parents have agreed to call her Suzzane." She paused for a moment to be sure she had Pat's attention. Then she went on, "I think you would like them a lot, Mrs. Vohwinkel. They own a construction company, and they are Roman Catholic, just like you requested."

"What are they like? I mean, what are their personalities like?"

"Well, as you know, I can't tell you very much. They want their privacy strictly guarded. But I can tell you that they are very sweet, and they love children. I think Suzzane will be happy with them."

"That means a lot to me," said Pat, the tears now running, unchecked, onto her oversized jumper. "That's the only reason I'm doing this, you know—for her."

"I know. And I'll say this just one last time. You don't have to give her up at all. Are you absolutely sure you want to give up Suzzane completely and for the rest of your life?"

"Yes. I'm absolutely sure."

The social worker looked kindly into Pat's eyes. "Is there anything else I can do for you?"

"I do have one more question," said Pat. "Is there any way I could get reports on how Suzzane is doing? I mean, in a general way."

Mrs. Godwin paused, choosing her words carefully to be as honest as possible. "We do sometimes get reports on some of the children who have been placed by our agency. Why don't you give me a call a couple of times a year, and I'll see what I can dig up for you. I can't promise I'll have a lot, but I may be able to tell you something now and then."

"I would be glad for whatever you could tell me."

Pat sat in her room for a long time after the social worker left, not because there was no nurse to take her to the hospital entrance, but because this room—their room—was her last earthly tie to her only daughter. Finally, when she had cried her last tear and summoned what strength she had left, she forced herself to get out of the chair and walk out the door.

"Good-bye, baby," she said. But there was no one to hear her.

chapter 2

"Mommeee!" squealed Harry, as he ran down the narrow sidewalk and leaped into his mother's hungry arms. She twirled him around until they were both dizzy. Then she got a gleam in her eye as she planted a kiss on his right cheek and said, "I love you a bushel . . ."

Harry smiled and squinched up his shoulders, trying to hide his neck.

". . . and a peck . . ." With that, she kissed the other cheek. Then she paused and watched him draw his shoulders even tighter, in anticipation of what was to come.

". . . and a gickle in the neck!" She pounced upon his helpless neck with such ticklish kisses that the ecstatic boy nearly passed out with laughter and delight.

"How's my little man?" she asked, when he had caught his breath.

"Good!" answered Harry. "But I missed you. Real bad. You were gone so-o-o long!"

"I know I was, honey, but I'm here now, and we're together. And we're gonna stay that way forever."

She carried the boy up the stone steps and into the kitchen of the small row house where she had lived with her sister, Helen, since the pregnancy had caused her to stop working several months before. Pat gingerly settled herself onto one of the kitchen chairs. That gickle in the neck had been a little too much for her.

"You doing okay?" asked Helen, as she filled two glasses of ice with Pepsi and placed them on the table.

"As well as can be expected."

"And how are you doing about Suzzane—I mean, with the adoption and all that."

"I'd really rather not talk about it, if you don't mind."

"Oh, sure. I understand." Helen quickly changed the subject. "You should see what Harry has learned to do." She pointed to a paper fastened to the front of the refrigerator with a small magnet. Scrawled across the page in bold, green crayon was a reasonably good facsimile of a letter *H*.

Pat smiled. "Smart kid."

Helen winked. "He gets that from his aunt." She settled herself on the chair opposite Pat and continued: "Have you thought about what you might like to do, now that you will be able to work again—after you recover a bit, of course."

"Actually, I have. This probably sounds silly, but I was watching Perry Mason the other day, and I thought I might really like to be a secretary. Of course, I'd need to get my

GED first. Doesn't it sound fun, though?" Pat sat up in her chair and tilted her head in her best imitation of Della Street. "Pat Street, Behind-the-Scenes Hero and Right-hand Woman to the most famous detective in town."

The two sisters erupted in laughter.

"Seriously, though," continued Pat after a while, "I think secretarial work is so interesting."

"You'd need some training at Bryant and Stratton or something. How would you pay for it?"

"I don't know. It's a dumb idea, I suppose. I'll probably just get another waitressing job."

"Waitressing's not a bad job, Pat. The customers always like you, and you get tipped well."

"Not enough to take care of Harry the way I'd like to. What I really wish, is that I could just stay home with him and have a man provide for us."

"If you find a man like that, be sure to introduce me to his brother!"

Pat took it easy for the next few days. But she couldn't stay at Helen's forever. It was time to get on with her life. It was already mid-August, too late to sign up for classes— even if she could find a way to pay for them—so she began to scan the want ads. Within a week, she noticed an ad that seemed to be a good fit for her: *Wanted: Experienced waitress for a busy restaurant on the West Side. Responsible persons only need apply.* Responsible person, busy restaurant; that sounded exciting. And she could take the bus to the West Side. She called and set up an interview for the next day.

Pat took the bus to Delaware Avenue, and then transferred to a second bus that took her to the West Side. It wasn't a bad ride, for all that. The second bus let her off right in front of the restaurant.

The Open House, as the restaurant was called, was a medium-sized establishment with several tables, and a row of booths running along the side wall. Pat surveyed the place from the outside, hoping no one of any importance spied her peeking in through the window. Her attention was suddenly arrested by a man perched on a ladder a few feet away from her. He was apparently changing a light bulb in the sign above the door.

"Hello," said the man, as he climbed down to the sidewalk. "Need any help?"

"Oh, no," she responded. "I am supposed to meet the owner of the restaurant here at 2:30, but I'm a little early, so I thought I'd just have a look at the place before I go in."

"Smart gal. You wouldn't want to work at a place that doesn't measure up. Your name Pat by any chance?"

Pat looked wary, then thoroughly embarrassed, as she sheepishly nodded. "Yes."

"Well, then, let's head in together, Pat. I'm Sam Ciminelli, and I'm the fella you came to talk to." He smiled and held out a friendly hand. Pat smiled and shook his hand, then followed Sam, and his ladder, into the restaurant.

Sam and Pat hit it off immediately. He liked her attitude, and she liked his style. It was looking like she might not find waitressing again so bad, after all.

"I'll be looking for you in the morning, then," said Sam after they had toured the restaurant and discussed the particulars of the job.

"I'll be here," she answered with a smile.

Sam paid well, and the customers were generous with their tips. It didn't take long for Pat to save enough money for a security deposit on her own apartment. And, while she was grateful for all Helen had done for her, she was ready to be out on her own—maybe.

Pat had never really been alone; well, not for long, anyway. There had always been someone around. Her childhood home had been full of children, too many of them at times. Then, there was Harry. Not little Harry—whose full name was Harry Bateman, III—but his father, Harry Bateman, II. He was the most handsome man Pat had ever seen. She had been so in love with him that she had left home to marry him when she was only seventeen. Life with Harry had been exciting. But it didn't last very long. Harry died in a motorcycle crash when Pat was only 21. She had met Vince soon after that. *Vince, ooh!* She shuddered. Why had

Pat at sixteen. She left home to marry at seventeen.

she thought of him? No, it would be better to be alone with little Harry than to live with a man like Vince again.

Pat found an apartment a few buildings away from her older sister, Mary. It had two bedrooms and a bathroom upstairs, a kitchen and living room downstairs—and the backyard had a fence. It was perfect for her and Harry. But it was a rather lonely place. Mary was busy with her own three children, and as much as Pat adored Harry, she longed for adult companionship. Maybe she should have some people over for a night of cards, she thought, after she had spent one-too-many evenings alone.

Pat invited Ma, Mary and her husband Dave, her brother Eddie, and his wife Jane—and all the assorted offspring—to a long evening of snacks, card games, and good company.

Pat's kitchen was rather compact. Her table was even smaller. Still, the Vohwinkel adults loved cards. They squeezed their chairs so close together that they were bound to become either bosom buddies, or sworn enemies, before the evening was over.

And the children? Mary's girls and Eddie's oldest daughter soon followed Harry into the less crowded rooms in the apartment. There was enough mischief to be had in that unexplored expanse to last them well into the evening.

Pat, as the hostess, had the end seat, not because it was a seat of honor, but because it was the only one from which someone could reach the refrigerator to grab refills of Pepsi. Beside her sat Jane, who was trying, in vain, to occupy her two-month-old daughter Cheryl.

"Let me take her for a while," said Pat, holding out her arms for the baby.

"Thanks," said Jane.

"There you go, shh. Sh. You're fine," Pat cooed, as she patted and stroked and cuddled the baby. Memories of Suzzane suddenly washed over her. Cheryl was only four days older than Suzzane. *Is this how my daughter looks?* she wondered. *Does she smell as sweet? Could her new mother possibly love her as much as I do?*

A few silent tears welled up in Pat's eyes, and she held the baby closer. Deep, unquenchable longing flooded her soul. Would she ever get over her grief for Suzzane, or be able to hold a little one without remembering?

Mary noticed Pat's tears and gave her a sympathetic smile, as much as to say, "Hang in there, Pat. You're gonna make it."

The next morning, before Harry woke up, Pat set to the task of cleaning up after the party. As she put the extra chairs away, she was struck by such a vivid memory of what it had felt like to hold a baby in her arms that she was nearly overcome by the magnitude of her loss. Her arms were so empty now, her house so quiet. How could she have given up her daughter!?

She hurried to the closet and pulled Mrs. Godwin's business card out of the purse that hung there. She dialed the number and sat down. Someone picked up at the other end of the line.

"Family Services. This is Mrs. Godwin. How may I help you?"

"Hello," said Pat, in an unsteady voice. She composed herself and spoke again. "You might not remember me, but my name is Pat Vohwinkel, and I gave up a baby girl for adoption in August."

"I remember you, Pat. What can I do for you?"

"I was just wondering if you had heard any news about Suzzane."

"Yes, we are still monitoring her, and she is doing fine. She's healthy and developing on schedule and seems to be very well adjusted to her new home."

Pat was surprised by her mix of emotions. She wanted Suzzane to be happy, but it was hard to think that her child might have forgotten her already. Had she become nothing more than *the birth mother?*

"That's good," she said. She was talking on automatic now, and it was the expected answer. "Is there anything else?"

"No. It seems your daughter has found a good home."

"Well, thank you." Pat supposed she said good-bye as well, but the conversation blurred in her mind after that.

Harry came into the room. He was still dressed in his footie pajamas. Pat dried her eyes and scooped him into her arms.

"Mommy is crying?" he asked.

"A little bit, but I'm done now," she said. He took it as the truth and moved on to the next topic. "Can I have Fruity Pebbles?"

"You betcha! Let's go downstairs, and you can eat them in your pajamas."

Caring for Harry was a balm for Pat. He was still young enough to tolerate a bit of babying—especially when he was tired or sick—or wearing his footie pajamas. Pat whispered a prayer to God—wherever He might be out in that vast and lonely universe: "Dear God, if You can see my Suzzane, take care of her. And whatever You do, please don't ever take my Harry away."

chapter 3

It was autumn of 1966. Pat had been pulling afternoon shifts at the Open House for a couple of weeks, when she noticed one customer who seemed to have an amazing ability to drink coffee by the potful. His name was Pete Golwitzer. Pete came in for lunch just about every day, and he always sat at one of her tables. He ate his food quickly enough, but then he would linger for cup after cup of strong black coffee. It didn't take Pat long to figure out what attracted him to those particular cups of coffee.

"Say, Pat," he would say, as she passed by his table on the way to serve other customers, "you pour the best cup in town. How about refilling my cup next time you fly by." On the next pass it would be, "Well, Pat, my cup has gone dry again. Why don't you come on over here and fill it up for me." Even a child could see that Pete was smitten. No other coffee in town would do.

Pat wasn't sure about him at first. She liked the attention well enough—who wouldn't? But Vince had made her wary. He, too, had "liked her coffee." It was an old line, and waitresses knew it well. But Pete seemed different somehow. He was sweet in a boyish sort of way and friendly to everyone. Pat liked that in him. Pete liked children too. He had three of his own by a previous wife. Two of these had died of suspicious circumstances. It was believed his wife had violently abused at least one of them. It was a sad story, and it worked on Pat's emotions. She had lost a child, and he had too. Both of them shared a similar grief.

"Well, Pat," Pete said one afternoon when the restaurant was rather quiet, and she had a moment to relax, "we've been meeting here these past few weeks," *(We have?* she thought) "and I was thinking it was time we went on a date somewhere special. There's an exhibition of monster trucks this Saturday, and I can get us in for free. You mind finding empty seats after the show starts?"

Pat smiled. He certainly was a down-home kind of guy. But what could it hurt? He seemed innocent enough. "Sure, Pete. I think that would be fun. Do you have a car, or are we going to meet at the exhibition?"

"Do I have a car? Do I have a car! Of course I have a car. And if I didn't, I could always borrow one." With that, he raised his chin as though grievously insulted and gave her a cute little wink that was to become his trademark. How could a woman resist?

Pete pulled up in front of Pat's apartment that Friday in a rusted, blue sedan of indistinguishable make and model. It loudly announced its lack of a muffler. (It had probably fallen off during the same mishap that had ejected the rear bumper and dented the left, rear quarter panel.) *Mmm.* She said to herself. *Class. Maybe he is planning to enter it into the monster truck competition.* Amazingly, the clunker drove. And it wasn't nearly as loud on the inside as it had been from the outside.

Pat had never been to a monster truck exhibition. And she wouldn't be sad if she never got to attend another. They were way too loud, and the entire auditorium was filled with exhaust fumes. But Pete enjoyed himself so much that she couldn't help picking up some of his happy mood. Besides, it had been a long time since anyone had bought her popcorn. Pete bought her a large box and let her eat the whole thing.

"Wasn't that great?" asked Pete as they walked to the car. "Man, I'd love to drive one of them things!"

Pat smiled, not because she agreed with his sentiments, but because his enthusiasm was infectious. No, Pat didn't care much for monster trucks, but she was beginning to like a man who did.

Pete took Pat out a lot after that. To more exhibitions, to the park, to grocery store grand-openings. And, the more he took her out, the more she liked him.

"Pat," Pete said to her one evening as they sat by the river, "I think we've been dating long enough. You know as well as I do that we want to be together. I'm not much of a poet or nothing, but I think it's obvious; you and me should get married. What do you think?"

Pat was ecstatic. Finally, a man who loved her and who would care for her. Someone who would be there for her

Pete and Pat Golwitzer

when she needed him. And she could stay home and raise Harry. Life was looking up.

Pete and Pat Golwitzer got an apartment in the same low-income housing project in which her parents and two of her sisters lived. It was a row house, in a cluster of buildings that all faced a common hardtop courtyard. A few mature trees dotted the courtyard to offer a hint of shade, but the place was hot in the summer, bitter in the winter, and filled with crime and deceit the whole year through.

Children played in the courtyard. Neighbors shouted to each other (or at one another) from small cement porches that provided access to each separate door. It was a lively place, a rough place, but for Pat it was home.

They had been living there only a few months when Pat realized she was expecting her third child. Another baby! What a joy. She still thought of Suzzane quite a bit, but the pain of losing her, which had been gradually diluting with the passing months, was now replaced, in large part, by the joyful expectation of another baby.

With a lighter heart, Pat called Mrs. Godwin. It had been almost a year since Suzzane was born; perhaps the social worker would have some news.

"No, Mrs. Voh . . . , er, I mean Golwitzer, we have not had any news about Suzzane for a while," she said over the telephone. "As far as we can tell, the adoptive parents decided not to finalize the adoption, and Suzzane was placed with another couple."

"What other couple?" asked Pat. "Why didn't they want her? Is something wrong?"

"I have very little information about the transfer. But I don't think there is anything wrong with Suzzane; just that, for some reason, custody was transferred to another couple. I'm sorry. That's all the information I have."

"Just tell me who knows more about it; I'll call them."

"I'm sorry, Mrs. Golwitzer. There is nothing more I can do. The papers are sealed."

"Isn't there anything I can do?" The desperation in Pat's voice was heartbreaking.

"There is a directory that you can join. It's not a guarantee that you will ever hear from her. But if Suzzane, or her new parents, ever want to contact you, they can look up your information in the directory, and then act on it, if they choose to do so. They may also choose to place their information on the directory for you to find. It's all a voluntary thing. I'm sorry. That's the best I can do."

Pat was devastated. She had given up Suzzane with the understanding that she could get regular progress reports. But her child had somehow slipped deep into the system, and there was nothing she could do about it. She joined the registry.

chapter 4

P at's third child, a boy, was born in November of
1967. He was robust and healthy. Pete named him
Brian Edward, in memory of the young Brian he
had lost to the abusive temper of his first wife. They had
another boy, just two years later, and named him Eddie.
Pat was content—and very busy. Keeping an eye on six-
year-old Harry, while feeding and diapering a toddler and
an infant, left her with little time to herself.

Toward the end of Eddie's first year, he developed an
unrelenting case of diarrhea. It continued for months,
driving Pat to near exhaustion as she diapered and cleaned
up after him between visits to the doctor. Her exhaustion
was heightened by the fact that she was expecting another
baby.

Pat had just finished changing Eddie's diaper—again—
when she noticed how quiet the house was. That was never
a good sign when Brian was around. She went to look for
him.

She found her three-year-old lying on the carpet in the living room. He was still and quiet. She picked him up. He was burning with a fever. Pete was at work, so Pat called a friend to drive them to the hospital. It was the quickest way to be seen when she didn't have an appointment.

They drew some blood, and then told her to have a seat in the waiting area. As she sat holding the sick child on her lap, she couldn't help but worry. What was wrong? Was she going to lose him like she had lost Suzzane?

Pat had seen a dead baby once. It was a dreadful thing. She had been only sixteen or seventeen when a virus ran through the housing project. It sickened many babies. One mother didn't understand how important it was to keep her baby hydrated. He didn't want to drink, so she didn't force him.

The last time Pat saw that baby was at his funeral. He lay so still and peaceful in his tiny casket. She thought, *All I have to do is shake him, and he'll wake up.* But he didn't wake up. Not ever again.

Her thoughts came back to the present. Brian was on her lap, still and peaceful. She shook him. He stirred. Whew!

Then she thought of God. Did He care about babies dying? Surely, He must. Then why had He let that little baby die? None of it made sense.

Pat remembered the prayer that had been printed on the back of the dead baby's funeral card. It was Psalm 23. She didn't know the prayer by heart, but she remembered enough of it to draw a little comfort from its promises.

Though I walk through the valley of the shadow of death, I will fear no evil: for thou art with me.

The shadow of death. Is that where Brian was? She prayed, wondering if God would hear a woman like her, a woman who didn't pray very often and who never went to church.

God, I know I don't deserve anything from You. But there is no one else to ask. I can't stand the thought of losing Brian. Please!

Brian was still alive. Still, and peaceful, but still alive.

The doctor came into the room. At the same moment, Brian fell into unconsciousness. The doctor picked him up in his strong, gentle arms.

"Mrs. Golwitzer," he said, "you have a very sick boy. He has mononucleosis. I have arranged for him to stay here at the hospital where we can give him medications and monitor him. But you will have to keep yourself away from him for a while. The disease could hurt your unborn baby."

"That's okay!" she said, with unmasked relief. "I'll stay away, just save my boy."

"I think he's going to be fine. He just needs medicine and time to recover."

The doctor left Pat alone in the waiting room with empty arms.

Brian recovered and, within a few weeks, he was back to his spunky, mischievous self. It seemed that God did care about babies.

Baby Number 4 was born in February 1971. It was another boy. They named him Peter.

Pat's boys. Left to right: Eddie, Harry, Peter, and Brian.

Pat adored her boys and lavished on them as many kisses and "gickles-in-the-neck" as they could stand.

She was not as careful to give them discipline. She didn't know how. Pat's father had been so abusive that she did not understand how to wrap her love in a spanking. The worst punishment she ever considered doling out was, in her own words, "Fifty lashes with a wet noodle." Oh, she would scold or withhold privileges at times, but when forced to choose between strictness or mercy, she invariably chose mercy.

Several members of the family teased her about her over-merciful parenting style, especially as the boys grew older.

"You'd better stop that," they would tease the boys, "or your mother will warn you again!"

This was hard on Pat, who wanted, more than anything, to do what was right for her children.

Perhaps, if Pete had taken it upon himself to train the boys, things might have been easier, but he didn't know much about parenting either.

Besides, Pete was growing aloof. He had become surly and distrustful—even angry at times. His outbursts scared Pat.

To escape the turmoil, and earn a little money at the same time, she began selling Tupperware. It didn't bring in as much as waitressing, and it wasn't nearly as glamorous as secretarial work, but it was something to do, and Pat enjoyed it. Pete saw it as a threat to his manhood.

"Are you going to another one of your parties?" he sneered. She had her show-kit in her hand and was about to walk out the door.

"Yes. Paula has gathered a little group of the ladies she works with."

"Why are you always going to those things anyway?"

"You know very well why I go. You don't give me enough money to buy the things we need. Besides, it gives me a chance to dress up and see some of my friends."

"Friends? Ha! You don't have any friends. They're just a bunch of lazy women looking to dump their kids on their husbands."

"Don't say that, Pete. Besides, Harry looks after the boys while I'm gone, so you've got nothing to complain about."

She would have thought her husband was drunk if she didn't know better. She had begun to suspect that he was suffering from some kind of bizarre mental illness.

"Well, I should be back by ten." With that, she shut the door.

By the time Peter was two years old, Pete had become unbearable. One Saturday afternoon, when all the children had gone out to play in the courtyard, their parents gathered to play poker in the basement of a neighbor named Skip. Pat was there. So was her mother and her sister Helen. Pete didn't want to go.

They played for hours. By the time the game broke up, Pat had become one of the big winners. She was carrying home her winnings in a bucket when Pete accosted her in the courtyard.

"I know what you've been doing down there all day. You've been having an affair with Skip. You good-for-nothing cheat!"

Pat couldn't believe what she was hearing. Where did he get such notions? "Yeah, right!" she retorted. "I was down there with Ma and Helen and all the neighbors, having an affair with Skip. You're crazy, Pete."

Pete reached out to grab Pat, or maybe he actually pushed her. In any case, his grasp was sudden and violent, and he knocked the bucket of change out of Pat's hands. The money spilled all over the pavement, a further announcement to all the neighbors that Pete was wild with anger.

Now Pat was angry too. "Don't you lay a hand on me," she screamed, "or it'll be the last hand you ever lay!"

All the neighbors were standing around, watching and whispering. Were they wondering if Pete's accusations were correct, that Pat was being unfaithful to Pete? Pat was humiliated and angry. No way would she put up with Pete any longer, and she told him so.

Pat and the boys applied for a separate apartment, and they were assigned another one on the same courtyard. Pete was allowed to stay where he was. Not only was this an extremely awkward arrangement, but when Pat moved out, Pete was left with all the furniture. He had the beds, the clothes, the food, even the toys!

It took the police (and several of the neighbors) to persuade Pete to allow Pat to take those things which she and the boys needed. That night, she sat in her partially-furnished bedroom and cried.

Pat and Pete got divorced shortly after she moved out. Widowed, abandoned, empty-armed, now divorced—life was turning out to be nothing but an endless series of dreadful grief and bitter disappointment. *Is it even worth living?* she wondered.

chapter 5

March came, and filthy slush, flung from the wheels of passing cars, had turned the snow a dismal gray. Lighter flakes were caught up by the wind and flung like frozen darts across the courtyard. Pat was glad she didn't have any errands to run.

Someone knocked at her front door. "Who would be out in this?" she wondered.

She opened the door to a woman in a long black coat and matching hat that looked like something from the pages of Mary Poppins (or the Queen of England). It was Pat's first mother-in-law, Mrs. Bateman.

"Well, of all the days to be out! Come on in, and let's get you warmed up." She took Mrs. Bateman's coat and laid it on the radiator to warm while it dried.

Harry entered the room. He was eleven now and still loved seeing his grandmother. She was the only tie he had to his father. "Hi, Grandma. It's good to see you!" He gave her a warm hug.

"It's good to see you too. I brought something for you and your brothers. Why don't you take them and run along. I need to talk to your mother for a while." She handed him a bag of Hershey's miniature candy bars. Harry was too old to need bribing, but he understood that his grandmother wanted to talk with his mother in private. He ran off to keep his brothers out of their way.

"I have come to offer you a proposition," began Mrs. Bateman when the two women were comfortably seated on the couch. "As you know, I have set aside a little money for Harry. I would like to use some of that to provide a down payment on a house in a more suitable section of town. This is a rather dangerous area, especially now that there is no man in the house. I think you and the children should move. There is a duplex for sale on the South Side. I believe you could live with the boys downstairs and charge enough rent for the upper flat to pay your mortgage."

Pat didn't know what to say. She had never dreamed of owning her own home. Or imagined what it would be like. Could she really pay for a house merely by collecting rent from a tenant?

"Wow. I hardly know what to say. I mean, I wouldn't have the slightest idea how to go about such a thing."

"It's not that hard. A friend of mine is a realtor. She will be able to guide you through the entire process. You don't have to decide today, of course, but think about it. We can get started as soon as you give us the go-ahead."

With that, Mrs. Bateman arose and retrieved her coat, now warm, from the radiator. "It's a good opportunity, Pat. I'll be waiting for your call," she said, as she made her way to the door and disappeared into the cold.

Pat sat speechless. *A home of our own. On the South Side. Who would ever have thought it!*

The house was as splendid as Mrs. Bateman had made it out to be, a two-story duplex on a tree-lined street of privately-owned homes. Everything that they needed for their family of five was on one floor, except for the laundry, which was in the basement. And the entire front of the building was spanned by a deep, come-and-sit-a-spell kind of porch. What a place to raise her boys! They moved in before the last of the blossoms fell from the bushes on the front lawn.

Her new surroundings infused Pat with a sense of hope. Maybe here her boys would have a future. The streets were certainly safer than those back in the housing project, and the neighborhood children seemed nicer too. Some of them even had curfews.

It didn't take long to rent the upstairs apartment. Mrs. Bateman knew of a single mother who needed a place right away. Her name was Maureen Whelan, and she had three children. It seemed like an ideal situation for everyone involved.

Pat threw herself into being a good mother. She scrubbed all the rooms with Pine Sol and sewed matching bedspreads and curtains for the bedrooms. She baked cookies and made delicious meals like pork roast with mashed potatoes, and big bowls of sweet corn swimming in butter. The boys responded in kind, telling Pat she was the best mom in the whole world.

Pat's mother came to stay with them for a few weeks that summer. As she preferred to sleep on the couch in the living room, accommodations weren't a problem, but she brought a level of tension that hadn't been felt in the Golwitzer family since Pete had left. It wasn't that she was cruel to anyone, nor that she was an ungrateful houseguest, but she nagged the boys.

"Put a shirt on," she told Peter one summer evening when his mother had gone down to the basement to throw in a load of wash.

"Mom said I didn't have to wear one because it's so hot," he answered.

"Harry, come pick up these Legos before someone trips over them," she told the oldest son one afternoon when Pat was cooking in the kitchen.

"Mom told Brian to clean them up," he replied.

"Well, he's not here, so you should do it."

Sometimes she even nagged the boys when Pat was in the room. "Quiet down!" she yelled at Eddie and Peter one day when they were running through the house pretending to be race cars.

Pat defended them. "Ma, they're fine."

"You shouldn't let them play so loud. They're gonna bother the neighbors."

"Boys need to play."

"Well, they play too loud."

Pat felt sorry for the boys, but she didn't know how to defend them. It was her mother, after all, and she wanted to be respectful of her, but this was her boys' home.

Besides, there wasn't much chance of the boys disturbing the neighbors—Bruce bickered so loudly with his brother and sister upstairs, there was no way they were going to hear any stray noises through the floor.

Pat began to snack, at times, as a way of easing the tension and depression of her circumstances, and she began to put on a bit of weight—not so much as to make her unattractive, but more than she was comfortable with. It was a relief when Ma finally went home.

The summer passed quickly, for all that, and September came; the boys began another school year. They had just left for school one morning when Maureen knocked at her door.

"Good morning," said Pat as she gestured for the woman to come into the living room. Though Maureen was her tenant, Pat treated her like a friend.

"No thanks," replied Maureen. "I can't stay. I just thought you'd like to know that Harry has been tearing up the bushes down at the corner."

"That doesn't sound like Harry."

"Well, the pieces are all over the sidewalk, and Bruce says Harry is the one who's been doing it."

Pat would have been concerned if she had thought it could be true, but Harry? He was always so respectful of other people's things. "Are you sure he said Harry did it? I find that hard to believe."

"Bruce says he saw him do it."

"Well, I'll talk to him when he gets home, but I'm sure there's been some mistake." The younger boys came in before Harry. Pat met them at the door and asked them what was happening to the bushes.

"Bruce has been cutting off branches and building little houses with them," said Brian without hesitation.

"Yeah," added Peter. "He's got a new knife."

"Bruce carries a knife around?" asked Pat.

"No, it's just a pocket knife," answered Peter.

Pat smiled at the boy's logic. "Okay. Go change into your play clothes."

When Harry came in, she questioned him too. His story matched that of his brothers. She was relieved.

As the weeks went by, Bruce accused Harry of doing other things. Someone had scribbled nasty words on the side of the house in magic marker. Bruce said he saw Harry do it. A stolen bike was found hidden behind their garage. Bruce said he saw Harry steal it. It was mighty funny how Bruce always seemed to be in just the right place to see Harry commit his varied crimes.

Pat defended Harry whenever Bruce or Maureen accused him—which was getting to be rather often—but she couldn't prove his innocence. Having tenants was turning out to be more stressful than she had imagined.

Thankfully, Maureen could be ignored most of the time. Pat tried to keep to herself and not think about her too much. She was glad when November came; Thanksgiving and Christmas were her favorite times of the year.

She taped some colorful turkey pictures in the windows and phoned her sister. Mary's family and her own had grown closer as the children had entered their school years; how nice it would be if they could come to her new home for Thanksgiving.

Dave and Mary Noonan and their children arrived well before noon on Thanksgiving Day. There was no sense shortening the celebration by starting it late. The girls each carried in a pie; it was the only thing Pat let them bring.

"Mmm, it smells good in here," remarked Mary.

"When do we eat?" added Dave.

Pat smiled. The house did smell good. She loved when her company enjoyed themselves. "The turkey's still got a half hour, but there are plenty of goodies on the snack table. Help yourself." The children had already found the bowls of chips, nuts, and party mix that Pat had put out in anticipation of their arrival.

"No thanks," said Dave—who didn't seem to notice the pile of nuts he had just picked up. "I'm saving all the room I can for the turkey." Pat looked at the nuts in Dave's hand and smiled at Mary. Dave went on chewing.

The weather was mild that year, so the children went outside to play after dinner. They had been out a few hours when Maureen knocked at the door. She stood in the foyer surrounded by several children, some hers, some Pat's, some Mary's. She was holding her youngest child, Lisa, in her arms. The girl was nursing a swollen lip and crying.

"I've tried to be patient with that boy of yours," Maureen growled, before Pat had time to say hello. "But when he starts bullying the younger ones, I have to draw the line!"

Pat stood there, half-worried about the child's lip and half-incredulous. Defensive anger began boiling inside her at the realization that Maureen was accusing Harry again. "What happened?" she asked.

"He pushed her down onto the sidewalk; that's what happened!"

"Did anyone see him do it?"

"That's all you ever care about. I'm sick of you always defending him, and I want it to stop!"

Pat started to cry. The woman's words, and the way she hurled them, struck hard. Dave looked at the children standing behind Maureen in the foyer. "Luanne, did you see what happened?"

His oldest daughter nodded. "We were all playing freeze tag, and Harry was it. Lisa just ran out in front of Harry when he was going to tag Brian. Then she tripped and smashed her lip on the sidewalk. Harry never touched her."

"He should have known better than to play tag with a three-year-old," interrupted Maureen. Dave ignored her, and looked at the rest of the children for more information.

"Lu's right," offered Eddie. "I seen it. Harry didn't do nothing to Lisa. She just fell by herself."

"You guys come on in here now," said Mary to the children. "We're gonna play inside for a while."

There didn't seem to be anything that would soothe the irrational woman at the door, so Dave said a polite, "Sorry the girl hurt herself, and have a nice day," and closed the door.

"She's constantly making accusations like that," said Pat, when they were back in the safety of her dining room. "She blames Harry for everything. I cringe whenever I meet her on the porch, wondering what she'll accuse him of next."

"She's just a bully," said Mary. "Don't give her the satisfaction of upsetting you. Just ignore her."

"It's hard to ignore a person who lives upstairs."

"Well, stay away from her as much as you can. Come on, let's have another piece of pie. There's still some of the apple crumb left." Pat consoled herself with a piece of pie, while the children ran off to play as cooperatively as they had done before Lisa had bruised her lip.

The adults wrapped up the evening with their traditional card game, as the children, exhausted but happy, fell asleep on every available couch and carpet. If it had not been for Maureen, it would have been the perfect day.

Christmas, then New Year, came and went, and with them went all the parties, cookies, and holiday dinners that mark the season as special. Pat noticed her clothes fit more snugly than before, so, about the second week in January, she stepped on the scale. She had gained five pounds. Five pounds. They came on so easily, but were so hard to take off. She decided to make an appointment with her doctor. Maybe he knew of some way to help.

"Have you been under any unusual stress lately?" asked the doctor after he had examined Pat.

Pat chuckled. "You want the whole story? I got divorced a few months ago, moved into a new neighborhood, and got a bully for a neighbor. It's about more than I can take."

"I thought it might be something like that. Not only has your weight gone up, but your blood pressure has too. I'd like you to go on a bit of medication for your nerves, as well as a diet pill that many people have been having success with."

"Whatever you suggest."

Pat filled the prescriptions on the way home and began taking them that day. She noticed a difference immediately. The diet pills calmed her appetite, and the medication calmed her nerves. Even Maureen seemed calmer when Pat was on the medicine—it must have been a miracle drug!

chapter 6

Pat and the boys had been on the South Side for a couple of years when she got a call from Helen saying that their father had cancer. It was really bad, and he wasn't expected to be around much longer. Pat didn't know if she should feel sorrow, or guilt, or guilt at not feeling more sorry.

Her relationship with her father was not at all good. It never had been. He had been severely abusive to all of his children, and there were times when she wished he would have died to spare them all the pain. Now he was dying. She was surprised at how much it hurt, now that it had come to that.

After Pat had said the things she was expected to say to such an announcement, she got a glass full of ice, doused it in Pepsi, and sat down on the couch to think. And to remember. The boys were all at school, so there was no one to interrupt her thoughts for several hours.

She searched her memory for some happy thought of her father, some smile, maybe on a birthday or at Christmas. There were none. All the pictures that flipped through her mind were of harshness, and fear, and pain.

She did remember escaping from him for a while, though. The taste of freedom had been glorious. She had been thirteen, a confident freshman, when she came in from school to find her father had returned after one of his many long and unexplained absences. It was not a pleasant discovery.

"Hello, Patsy. Come and give your father a kiss." Pat approached him with the ice-cold expression she always wore in his presence and applied the required token of affection. Fortunately, Mary and Helen came in right behind her, so she didn't have to wait around for a response.

She went up to the bedroom she shared with her four sisters. Carol and Janet were already there. They waited for Mary and Helen to join them. They didn't have to wait long.

Helen spoke first. "When did he get home?"

Carol answered. "Sometime today, I suppose. I wonder what name he's using this time." Their father never went by his real name; he was always Karl Schmidt or Fred Bogdan, or some other name that made him feel tough and proud and secret. They never did find out who he was running from more, the welfare authority or himself.

"Patsy," said Helen, "you'd better hurry up and pick up these clothes." She pointed to the nightclothes Pat had scattered on the floor in her hurry to get ready for school that morning.

"What does it matter? He's probably seen them already."

"Just pick them up," said Mary. "Why make trouble?"

The sound of their brother, Ed, closing his bedroom door was followed by a shout from downstairs. "Get your lazy carcasses down here now! Every one of you!"

"Here we go," said Pat. "Didn't think we'd have to wait long."

"We never do." Pat couldn't tell which of her sisters had responded—it could have been any of them.

The girls met Ed on the stairs, and they all descended so silently a visitor would not have known there was anyone beside Ma and their father in the house.

Mr. Vohwinkel, whatever his name was at the moment, awaited them in the kitchen, beside a trash bin that had garbage piled high above the rim. "I expect to find the house clean when I get home. Which of you was supposed to take out the trash today?" No one answered. They all knew it was Ed's week, but it was not their place to squeal on him.

"Which one, I said?"

Ed looked scared. He didn't have the courage to confess out loud, though. It didn't matter; his father saw the look on his face and zeroed right in on him. "You, boy?"

"Yes, sir."

With that pitiful confession, Mr. Vohwinkel swung his arm out and struck the boy with a loud crack. Then he struck him again, and again.

"Ma, make him stop!" pleaded Pat.

"You don't like me disciplining your brother, eh? Then maybe you'd like to take his beating for him." With that, he turned his blows on Pat and beat her until his rage was sated. She sank to the floor. He left the room.

Pat got up with a determination she had never felt before. She was thirteen and able to think clearly. No one should ever have to live through what just happened to her. And it would never happen to her again. Pat walked to the back door and quietly slipped away.

She had no coat or bag, no schoolbooks. What did it matter? She was alive and free, and she was never going back. She ran across the courtyard and slipped between the buildings. Her father was not behind her. Could it be that he really did not know she had escaped? Emerging into the next courtyard, she saw Sheila's door. Her father didn't know Sheila. Pat had met her only a few months ago, before her father's return.

She ran up to the door and pounded furiously. "Sheila, Sheila, are you home? It's Pat. Please open up; I need to come in right away."

The door opened. It was Sheila. Her mom was still at work.

"What happened to you?" she asked when she got Pat inside and closed the door. "Oh, look at your face! What happened?" Sheila's eyes teared up as she looked at her friend's bruised and swollen face and arms. "Oh, Pat, who did this to you?"

"My father."

"I thought he abandoned you."

"He does sometimes. He came back today. But I'm not going back. I'm never going back as long as he's there."

"Where will you go?"

"Anywhere."

"Well, for now, you can stay right here. I know my mom would say yes. He doesn't know you're here, does he?"

"No, he doesn't even know I left. And he doesn't know you. But I won't be able to stay here long. Everyone else knows where you live. He'll find out eventually."

Pat stayed with Sheila and her mom for four days. She did not leave the house during that time.

"Pat," said Sheila's mom, on the morning of the fourth day, "you can't stay here forever. If they find you, I could be charged with kidnapping. Besides, somebody would see you eventually, and then you would have to go home. I'll try to think of someplace else to take you by the time I get home. Don't worry though, we'll work out something."

Pat did worry. The adults in her life had thus far proven to be unreliable at best, and usually far worse than that. She liked Sheila's mom, but she didn't think the woman was likely to find a workable solution for the runaway. No, Pat was going to have to be gone before she returned from work.

She told Sheila her plan, and her friend urged her to wait around until she could skip out of school and come back to help.

"I have an idea," Sheila said, when she returned to the house an hour later. "Schiller Park has lots of bushes where you could hide out until it gets really cold. You could sleep there during the school hours so no one sees you, and I will visit you in the evenings." Pat agreed. The girls stuffed a pillowcase with food, warm clothes, and a flashlight. Then they went out the back door, which faced away from the courtyard. They darted between the buildings and made their way to the park, several blocks away.

It was not easy for two girls to travel through the streets unnoticed. But they took the alleys as much as they could and stayed under the shade of the trees the other times. Even so, two schoolgirls are rather conspicuous on the streets of a city on a school day, even when they are not marked by an overstuffed pillowcase.

They had just crossed the last street and entered the park, when they heard the squeal of sirens behind them. Both girls took to running immediately, but there was no place to go. After a short chase, they turned around, faced the squad car, and surrendered.

Sheila was returned home. Pat was arrested. After four days, she had been listed as a runaway; she had become a part of the system.

The policemen took Pat to the precinct station and told her to wait while they called her father to come pick her up.

"There's no sense calling him," she told them, "'cause I'm never going home with him again."

"He's your father, young lady. If he says you're going home, you're going home."

Pat could have told the officers about her father's abuse. She could have shown them her bruises, maybe even had him thrown into jail. But that was not her concern. All she knew was the instinctive drive not to be hurt by him ever again.

"I'm not going home!"

Somehow, the finality with which she uttered the words convinced the policemen that Pat was immovable. "All right then, if you won't go home, we will have to put you in the detention center."

"Then that's where I'll go."

Pat lived in the county detention center for girls for three months. She was given her own room—something she had only imagined—fed three square meals every day, and allowed to go to school at the center. Other than being locked up at night, it wasn't a bad deal. But the government wasn't in the business of providing housing for runaway children, and the day came when Pat was scheduled to appear before the judge.

The night before her hearing, Pat's father came to see her at the center.

"Pat," he said with earnestness in his voice, "listen, I know it gets a little hard on you kids when I have to discipline you. But I'm willing to change all that. I promise, if you come home, things'll be different. I promise. You'll see." Did he miss her—or was he just worried about his own skin?

Pat stared at her father. There was something else in the place that was supposed to feel love for him. Was it hate?

loathing? pity? How can a young girl sort out emotions like those?

"If you promise, then I will come. But I will hold you to that promise."

"You'll see. I'll keep my word."

That was the last Pat saw of her father for the next four years. He disappeared during that entire time. He kept his word.

chapter 7

Pat roused from her memories. She was on the couch. The ice in her glass had melted, and the Pepsi was warm and flat. Her father was dying. She was surprised to find that the thought made her sad. Very sad. He was her father, and he was dying. She would go see him.

The boys burst through the door. She hadn't heard them come up the porch steps. After they had told her all about their day at school, she took Harry aside and told him about his grandfather. He stood there for a while without saying anything. Mr. Vohwinkel had mellowed in his older years, and Harry knew a very different man than the one that lived in Pat's memories.

"I can watch the boys while you go to see him," Harry said, when Pat mentioned that she wanted to go see her father. "They don't know what's going on anyway, and you'll have a better visit." Pat was grateful for Harry's offer. This was not a good time to take the boys along.

Pat pulled into the familiar courtyard and parked in front of her parents' apartment. Everything looked dingier than it had twenty years ago—stark red-brick buildings void of awnings or shutters, cold cement steps in front of each gray steel door. Litter had blown and lodged against the steps, as if no one had noticed it there. The trees looked shabbier too.

Pat's parents, taken four years before her father's death.

She sat in the car for a while. How do you start a conversation with a dying man, or his wife? Guess she'd just begin with a hello, and let it go from there; it wasn't exactly something she could script out ahead of time.

"Hey," was all she said when Ma let her into the kitchen.

Then she looked at her father sitting in the chair facing the door. His parakeet was in its usual place on Dad's left shoulder. "Hi, Dad. I heard the news. How are you doing?"

"Fine. I'm fine, really. Just a little sore when I breathe too deep, you know." He gestured for Pat to take a seat across the table. She did. Ma joined them.

"They've been warning me to stop smoking for forty years now; guess they were right. They say it's in my stomach and liver already."

Pat shivered. "Can they do anything about it?"

"Doc says it's too far gone; just gotta wait it out, I guess."

"I'm so sorry. I mean, this is the kind of thing that happens to other people. Know what I mean?"

"Yeah, well, this time we're the other people."

Ma was fidgety. She got up again and walked over to the sink. "Can I get you some coffee, Patsy?" she asked.

"You know I don't drink coffee, Ma, but I'll take a glass of ice water, if you don't mind." Ma got the water and sat back down.

Pat looked at her father, really looked at him for the first time in years. He was older than she remembered, with a military haircut that had lost much of its raven luster. The skin beneath the tattoo of a hula girl that danced when he flexed his forearm was wrinkled and hung loosely on his withered frame. When had the rough sailor she had always called her father grown so old?

"I'm not real good at thinking of things to say at a time like this, Dad; I'm real sad about the news." Her eyes teared up, and she looked away.

"I'm sorry too," he said. "My life has been a waste. And I ruined yours too. I'm sorry, Pat. I'd undo it all if I could."

Pat forced a smile. "Things are okay with me. I've got four great boys, and I'm doing okay."

"Well, that's something."

She finished her water and rose from the chair. "Well, I've got to get home; Harry's alone with the boys. You take care, Dad. You, too, Mom. I'll come again soon."

Maureen Whelan was waiting in their joint foyer when Pat got home. She had that look on her face that made Pat wish she could fade into a vapor and fly away on the wind.

"Hi, Pat. Harry told me about your dad. I'm sorry to hear the news. I guess it's probably not the best time to tell you this, but you may as well have it all at once. Harry's been suspended for a week."

"From school?"

Maureen nodded.

"For what?"

"It seems he was putting some nasty graffiti on the steps out front."

"I suppose Bruce saw him do it."

"Don't get defensive. I'm only trying to help. But, yes, Bruce did see him do it. And so did a bunch of other kids."

"Well, I'll have to hear those other kids before I'll believe it."

Pat was in no mood to hear Maureen spout her garbage. She opened her front door, darted inside, and slammed the door behind her.

She barely had time to say hi to the boys and throw some frozen potpies into the oven when the phone rang. It was Mrs. Bateman.

"Hello, Pat. How are things with you and the boys?"

"They're fine. But we just found out that my father has cancer. They give him only a few months to live."

"I'm sorry to hear that. Is he in a lot of pain?"

"Not much yet."

"That's good. Yes, well, I'm calling about Harry. Mrs. Whelan has been telling me of all the trouble he has been in lately: fighting, stealing, now vandalizing and getting suspended from school. Why didn't you tell me all of this was going on?"

"Whatever you do, don't listen to Maureen. She's had it out for Harry since day one. She's forever making up some lie or other about him. Usually she's just looking to make excuses for something Bruce did."

"Surely the principal wouldn't suspend someone without cause. There are witnesses who say they watched Harry paint foul language on the steps. It's hard to believe they are all in league with Mrs. Whelan."

"Did you personally speak to these so-called witnesses? They probably don't even exist."

"Pat, I think you have been wearing blinders. It's time you opened your eyes to the fact that Harry has a problem. He needs you to give him a firm hand. He will be ruined if you don't."

Pat would be the first to admit that she was too lax with her boys. Maybe she should be a little stricter. But she knew Harry, and there was no way he could have done all the things Bruce had accused him of. Worse yet, Maureen had convinced Mrs. Bateman that Harry was a juvenile delinquent with a softhearted dupe for a mother.

She had thought she would like living in a duplex, that having neighbors who cared about their children would be a good thing. Truth was, though, life had been better back in the housing project. Sure, the folks there would shoot you as easy as talk to you, but they didn't harp all the time about how you raised your children. Besides, Pat fit better back there. It was where her friends were. It was where her family was. It was home.

"Boys!" she called to all corners of the house just a few seconds before the oven timer beeped to announce that their supper was ready, "come, help me get these pies to the table; then we'll have a little talk."

"First, I need to tell you that your grampa is very sick," she began, when they were each seated before their favorite flavor of pie. "He will probably live for only a few more months. I think we should be near him and Grandma."

Harry looked puzzled. "Will we go to live with them?"

"No, I was thinking how nice it was back in the project with all our friends. I thought we might move back there."

"To our old house?" asked Brian with excitement.

"I don't think they will give us the same apartment, but we might be able to get one close by. I'll call them tomorrow and see if they have anything open."

"Yay!" shouted Brian, who had fond memories of his early years in the project.

"Whoo-hoo!" joined in Eddie and Peter, not because they remembered much about their first home, but because Brian was so excited.

Harry did not shout, but he did smile. He, too, missed their old home where people had cared about him.

When Pat called the Housing Authority the next morning, she was told that there were no vacant apartments at the present. She was put on a waiting list.

chapter 8

P at's father declined quickly. By December, it was apparent that he had only about a month to live. Pat took her boys to see him as often as she could. Other times she went alone. It was hard to witness the last days of a man who had so many regrets. Pat's heart softened as she stood by and watched. She also feared for him. If Heaven and Hell were real places, and if people were assigned to their eternal station according to the deeds done while here on earth, then her father seemed the most hopeless of men. How could God forgive crimes as great as his? The questions worried her, but she had no answers.

She tried to pray for her father, but she didn't know what to say. How does one pray for a man like that? *Oh, God,* she cried in humble desperation, *You have no reason to listen to my prayers, but I beg You to take my father to Heaven when he dies—if it is at all possible.* That's all she could figure out to say; maybe God would find it good enough.

Mary and Dave and their fifteen-year-old daughter were talking with Ma in the kitchen when Pat entered her parents' home. After a quick hello, the teenager slipped off to the living room to see her dying grandfather. Pat took the opportunity to run upstairs and use the bathroom. On her way back down, she heard her father speaking to her niece. Something about his voice was different from usual—softer and more earnest. Was he crying?

". . . you don't know all the bad things I've done. I'm sorry, Sweetie, but I'm just too bad. God would never let your old grampa into Heaven."

"God doesn't care about how many bad things you've done. Well, He cares, but not like that. What God wants, is for us to be sorry."

"I am sorry. Very, very sorry. But being sorry doesn't undo things."

"Did you tell God you were sorry?"

"He wouldn't listen to me. Praying is for holy people."

"God listens to everyone, Grampa. How about I pray with you. Would that help?"

Pat was sure she heard him crying now. She didn't know that her father could cry. Tears welled up in her own eyes, as she listened to the teenager lead her father in a gut-wrenching prayer of confession and remorse. He really was sorry! Pat wiped her eyes and slipped back to the kitchen. Could Dad's prayer be enough to move God to overlook all the wretched things he had done to her?

Dad died a few weeks later. His last days, though filled with physical pain, were marked by a spirit of lightheartedness and joy. To all appearances, he really had made his peace with God. If such a thing were possible, that someone who had committed the list of crimes her father had, could truly be forgiven, then God was more amazing than Pat or any of her siblings, had ever imagined.

But they didn't talk about the subject openly. Religion was not something the Vohwinkels discussed, except maybe on Christmas or Easter, or when they wanted a swear word. There wasn't even a priest to talk to, because Dad hadn't shown any interest in religion until those last few days, and no one had thought to arrange as much as a memorial service. So, Ma and her children each went off to work out their private sorrow and questions alone.

Pat's emotions were a strange mix of grief, guilt, and turmoil. Painful memories competed with newfound sympathy for her father. She couldn't sleep. At her regular checkup, the doctor noticed her haggard appearance.

"You don't look well, Mrs. Golwitzer. Is that neighbor still giving you a hard time?"

"Yeah, but it's not that. My father died a few days ago, and I haven't been sleeping well."

"I can give you a little something to help with that. Let's see . . ." he looked down at her chart. "You're still taking the diet pills—your weight looks good—and the Valium. We'll add some Seconal and Tylenol-with-codeine to the mix."

"Oh, I'm not in any pain," said Pat.

"It also helps with tension. It will make things a little easier while you work through your father's passing. The

Seconal will help you get some sleep. It's standard therapy for situations like these."

Pat trusted her doctor. Why shouldn't she? He knew about drugs, and she didn't.

"Thanks so much," she said, as he handed her the prescriptions. "I really appreciate it."

When she went to get the prescriptions filled, the pharmacist asked if she had a death-wish.

"Why?" she asked.

"Well, if you take all these medicines the way they have been prescribed, there is a good chance they will kill you."

"Are you serious?" She could hardly believe her doctor would order medicines that would kill her. Still, the pharmacist specialized in drugs.

She cautiously added only the Seconal to the pills she took that night. The pharmacist might be right, but she needed some sleep. How much harm could a little sleeping pill do?

Sleep came quickly. Pat slept deeply and long. Too long. When she woke up the next day, it was well past dawn. It was even past noon. Pat had slept a full twenty-four hours. She was scared by the thought that she might never have awakened at all. Perhaps she was just catching up on all the sleep she had missed since her dad's death, but it seemed to be more than that. It was a good thing she hadn't taken the pain pill too!

Pat went right to the bathroom and flushed the new pills down the toilet. She would find some other way to fall asleep.

chapter 9

About the time life with Maureen had become almost unbearable, Pat got a call from the Housing Authority. There was a three-bedroom unit available on Edison Street. It was not the same courtyard on which they had lived before, but it wasn't far from there. And it was closer to Ma. She reserved the apartment, and called Mrs. Bateman to tell her she would be leaving the South Side. It had been a lovely gesture her mother-in-law had made, and she was grateful. But it was time for Pat and the boys to go home.

The apartment on Edison was identical to the one they had lived in before. It was just like Ma's too—three bedrooms and a bathroom upstairs, a kitchen and a living room downstairs, and a big basement for storing bicycles and other toys.

Dave and Eddie and some of their friends moved Pat's things to the new apartment. After they had left and she had put the boys to bed, Pat sat down on her couch, in what seemed like very familiar surroundings, and smiled. There was no one there to smile at; still, she smiled. *This must be what a bird feels like,* she thought, *when he escapes from his cage—delivered and airborne and free.* She hadn't realized how much living beneath Maureen had been sapping her joy, but now that she had broken free, she felt like the world had opened up before her.

It wasn't long before Pat made friends in the new courtyard. They were her kind of people, free and unassuming and easy to get along with. Before long, she was visiting and joining in their card games, just like they had all known each other for years.

One afternoon, during a game at the home of one of her new neighbors, Pat was introduced to Kevin Hardy. He was a bit younger than she, and had never been married. He was one of those sweet, unassuming men liked by everyone. Pat thought he was special. Kevin thought she was special too, and it wasn't very long before he moved into her apartment—not as a husband, or even as a live-in boyfriend, but as a good friend and member of the family.

Kevin was great to have around. He had a lighthearted outlook on life that was infectious. Pat and the boys loved him. He brought in a steady income too. Up to this point, Pat had been raising the boys primarily with the funds she got from the government—Pete had been very lax in sending child-support. Well, maybe lax was too mild a word; he hadn't been sending her anything. But Kevin had steady work driving dump trucks, limousines, and other vehicles for a small company, and he gladly used his money to care for Pat and her boys. Kevin was even a bit of a father figure to them. Not that he was a strict disciplinarian; he was more like an uncle or an older brother whom the boys respected and looked up to. A suggestion from Kevin was as likely to be obeyed as not, and that was a good thing for four boys who had spent many years without the influence of a father.

Kevin filled a big hole in Pat's life. He provided a framework of normalcy to her otherwise unpredictable life, and he helped her to make sense of things. He bought new sneakers for the boys, got them nice bicycles, and took Pat for rides in the big company dump truck.

"I can honestly say," remarked Pat on one of these spontaneous excursions, "that I've never gone out for ice cream in a dump truck before."

Kevin smiled broadly. "There's a first time for everything. Yours is gonna be a gravel sundae." Then he laughed at his little joke—the truck was currently filled with so much gravel that bits of stone and dust occasionally escaped the tarp that covered the bed and bounced to the road beneath them.

Kevin wasn't the only newcomer to the family. He hadn't been with them but a few months when Pat found herself the owner of a big, loud, chocolate-chip-cookie of a German shepherd named Princess. She was rather too large to live in the apartment, but the housing project didn't provide their residents with any yards to speak of, so the dog found a spot on the couch and considered herself a necessary part of the furniture.

Princess had lived with them just long enough for every member of the family to fall in love with her when they got a letter stating that dogs were not allowed in the housing project. They would have to either get rid of Princess or move.

"You can't get rid of Princess!" cried Peter. "We're her family."

"I know, honey, but we don't make the rules. I'll take her to a nice place, and she can have a new family there." Pat felt like a hypocrite. She knew that no one was likely to rescue such a large already-grown dog from the pound, no matter how adorable or lovable she was.

After the boys left for school one morning, Kevin drove Pat and Princess to the dog pound. Pat began to cry as she handed the leash to the clerk. "She's a really good dog. She's smart and loyal, and she doesn't bark too much. And she's great with kids. You'll be able to find an owner for her, won't you?"

"Pardon me for asking," said the clerk, "but it's obvious you really love the dog. Why are you giving her up?"

"We live in a public housing project and they don't allow pets. Either she goes, or we do."

"That's shameful!" said the clerk. "Cruel-hearted bureaucrats. Tell you what, you leave the dog here for the night, and I'll give you a receipt to prove that you turned her in. Then you can come back in tomorrow and re-rescue her. Know what I mean?" She winked.

Pat smiled. "Yeah, I do. Thank you. I really appreciate it."

Pat and Kevin drove straight from the pound to the housing authority and showed them the receipt that proved they had delivered their pet to the pound. And the next morning, as soon as the boys had left for school, they went back to the pound and *rescued* a beautiful shepherd-husky named Princess.

chapter 10

"Hey, Mom, Grandma's on the phone," called Brian from the top of the steps.

"Tell her I'll be right there." Pat finished loading the washing machine in the basement and hurried up to the living room to grab the phone. "Hi, Ma. What's up?"

"Where've you been? I've been calling for hours."

"We were out shopping. What's up?"

"That Damien from next door broke into the house last night and took all the money in my wallet."

"You're kidding!"

"Well, I thought I was losing my mind, because I was always losing things. I would set something down and, when I went to look for it, it was gone. Then, when I came in from running to the mailbox this morning, I heard someone upstairs. I guess he was trapped. I must have come home sooner than he expected. So he ran down the steps and out the back door, as pretty as you please. Didn't even try to hide his face. Bold as brass, just like that. It scared the wits out of me."

"I guess so. How did he break in?"

"All I can figure is, he came in the basement window."

"Didn't you have the basement door bolted?"

"I had been forgetting to lock it. But I sure will lock it tonight! Really, though, Patsy, I was hoping I could come and stay at your place tonight. He's got me scared to death, and I don't want to be here again when he comes. He would never have dared when your father was alive, but he's got no fear now. Doing drugs too, I guess. Never know what he'll do if he comes in here stoned."

"Get your stuff ready, and I'll have Kevin come get you as soon as he gets home."

"Nah, I can walk over. And I won't be needing to bring my stuff. I'll be leaving in the morning. I'm just afraid to be here alone at night."

"Yeah, sure. Well, the night would be fine. There's always room on the couch."

Ma came and spent the night. Then she returned the next evening, and the next, and the next. She only stayed from dusk till dawn, but she was as predictable as the sunset.

Ma was nice to have around at first. Pat liked the female company, and she could sympathize with Ma's fears. But, as she got comfortable being at Pat's, Ma began to nag at the boys like she had done that summer on the South Side. The difference this time was that Kevin was there to add his opinions to the mix.

The boys were used to living in a predominately male household, and they would frequently come downstairs to watch cartoons in their underwear. This irritated Ma's sense of decency.

"That's no way to walk around the house," she said to Eddie one morning when she caught him scantily clad. He looked at his mother for help.

"Ma, it's their house. They're only watching television. It's not like they're going outside."

"Well, they shouldn't be like that."

Then Kevin chimed in. "Patsy knows how to raise her boys; best to just leave it to her to do."

"It's none of your business; they're not your boys."

"I live here, so that makes it my business."

"Well, it's more my business than yours!"

These confrontations would escalate into arguments with the three adults shouting and the boys looking on.

"I'm just trying to help," Ma would finally say, in an effort to restore some sort of peace.

"Ma, please don't help!" Pat would plead. Then she would escape to her bedroom for the rest of the evening. There, at least, she could find peace.

Pat's life became an endless cycle of escapes from stress-filled evenings and attempts to recover the next day. But Ma always came too soon and stayed too long, and Pat's emotions steadily declined from tension, to depression, to despair.

After months of endless nagging and discord, Pat's emotions sank so low that she decided it would be easier to die than to go on living. She began planning a way to make a quiet and peaceful exit from a life that had become unbearable.

She was still taking Valium, a pill designed to calm a person. What if she could save up a big batch of pills and take them all at one time? That ought to make a peaceful end to things.

She kept her plan secret, half-embarrassed and half-worried that someone would find her out and try to stop her. So, when some friends asked her to go on a trip to play Bingo at a fancy casino in Atlantic City, she gladly accepted. It would be her last hurrah—one final chance to have a good time before ending a miserable life that had proved to be little more than grief and sorrow.

The casino was fun. Getting away with friends was a reprieve from her cycle of tension and escape. Perhaps if she could have stayed away longer, she might have recovered some of her zest for life. But the friends she was traveling with weren't the kind of friends she could share her struggles with. They were just friendly people who shared her love of playing Bingo. So, she enjoyed their company with the front half of her mind, while the back half continued to anticipate that final escape she would make when she returned home.

Pat took a longer time than usual saying goodnight to her children when she got home. Then she went upstairs, locked her bedroom door, and swallowed sixty-four tablets of Valium.

God reached down from Heaven that night and rescued poor, despondent Patricia Golwitzer. He did so as surely as

He had stepped down to part the Red Sea those many years ago. Without His intervention, no human being could have survived the influx of such a great quantity of sedatives, without fading softly but quickly into eternity. But God was not ready for Pat to enter eternity. He had a work to do in her soul before she made that crossing.

Pat awoke four days later. No one had intervened during that time—not Kevin, not Ma, not any of her children. But God had been with her, and that was all that mattered.

chapter 11

Pat did not know what to do with herself. She was faced with a life that she had tried to escape, and she had no plans for the future. Apparently, God had some reason for her to be alive. Perhaps, there was something He wanted her to do yet. One thing was for sure; if she was going to be of any use to God, or to anybody else, she was going to need to do something about her mother. She confronted her that evening.

"Ma, it's been really hard for me to handle the way you yell at the boys all the time. I'm going to have some kind of breakdown if you don't stop. Unless you can find a way to lay off them, I'm going to have to ask you not to spend the nights here."

Ma was obviously hurt by Pat's words, but they needed to be said. They should have been said a long time ago. But Ma was better after that. Perhaps she suspected that Pat's protracted disappearance had been more than a four-day pity-party. Whatever the reason, she harped on the boys much less after that.

Another year passed, during which Pat rebuilt her emotional reserves and regained an enthusiasm for life. Kevin was as kind and cheerful as ever, and as good a friend as anyone could want, though he and Pat were still nothing more than friends. Better still, Ma was finding the courage to stay at her own house some evenings.

The boys were growing so fast, though. Peter was ten already, and Harry was almost a man! She wouldn't have them much longer, it seemed.

A month or so before Harry's eighteenth birthday, Pat was awakened by his voice beside her bed. She could see the clock on the dresser behind him. It was 3:30 a.m.

"Mom," he said. He sounded weak and far away. Was that fear in his voice? "I think I need to go to the hospital."

Pat sat up instantly. "What's wrong?" She tried to shake off the grog from her sudden arousal. The last she knew, Harry had been out with his friend Dino.

"Dino wrecked his car, and I walked home. I thought I was okay. But when I went into the bathroom just now, I passed out and fell on the floor. I still feel kind of dizzy."

Pat jumped out of bed and went to wake Kevin. They threw on some clothes, and drove Harry to the county hospital which was only a few minutes away.

The nurses at the emergency department wheeled Harry into a room before Pat finished filling out his paperwork. He was x-rayed soon after that. When the doctor finally came in to tell them the results of the scans, he looked serious.

"Well, young man, it seems you have fractured your neck in two places."

"Thank God it's not broken!" exclaimed Pat.

The doctor turned toward her. "I'm sorry, Mrs. Golwitzer, but fractured means broken. Your son has broken the bones in his cervical spine. He will need surgery to repair them. We are preparing an operating room for him right now."

Pat leaned on the gurney. She was stunned. A broken neck! "Will he be paralyzed?" she asked.

"His responses are very good, but I can't promise anything at this point. Spinal injuries can be unpredictable. I can tell you this much: Someone was looking out for your son. The accident alone could have killed him. The fact that he walked home afterward and sustained another fall after that only increased his chances for permanent or life-threatening injury. I'd say your boy is lucky to be alive."

As they wheeled Harry out of the room and down the hall, Pat remembered her own dance with death the year before. She knew from experience that God could do miracles for regular people like her. She asked Him for one more. *Dear God, You've already done so much for me that I have no right to ask, but I beg You to heal Harry. He's so young; he's hardly had a chance to live.*

A broken neck was so serious. What if Harry was paralyzed for the rest of his life? Maybe he would be better off dead than paralyzed. And, if he was paralyzed, who would care for him? She wasn't going to be around forever. What would happen when she was gone? Pat amended her prayer. *God, I know I asked You to heal Harry, but I mean, will You please heal him fully? Please don't let him be paralyzed. It would destroy him.* She looked down. Who was she to ask so much? She never talked to God unless she wanted something, and she never went to church.

Church. She hadn't been to a church service since Harry's first Communion. She didn't remember how long it had been before that. Oh, she had gone when she was little—at least until Ma got mad at the drunken priest for refusing to give her copies of their baptismal records—something about them being poor and never putting any money in the offering. That was the day that Ma, who never swore if her life depended on it, stood in the middle of the street and cursed the priests. Pat hadn't been to church since. Now, here she was, begging God for help.

She remembered asking God to heal Brian when he was a baby, and God had answered her prayer. And He had pulled her through when she overdosed on those pills. So He obviously cared about her. She had a feeling He always cared, even when she forgot about Him for years. She thought again of the words on the dead baby's funeral card: *Though I walk through the valley of the shadow of death, I will fear no evil, for Thou art with me.* And she continued her prayer. *God, it is Harry's turn. Please save him.*

Harry came out of surgery with a metal halo bolted to his skull. The halo was attached by a cord to a pulley that applied constant traction to his spine. He could turn his head a bit from side to side, but he couldn't lift it off the pillow. The arrangement made him feel like a mouse in a trap.

For the next two weeks, Pat spent her days at the hospital and her nights at home. If she was not there for meals, Harry wouldn't eat. There was no dignity in being spoon-fed while lying on your back, and he wanted no one but his mother to do the humbling task for him.

Pat was tired from the long days, but it was an okay kind of tired. She was taking care of her son, her first child, and the task was not unpleasant. It seemed only yesterday that she had fed him in his high chair. She marveled that, grown as he was, caring for him was not a chore.

Harry needed another minor surgery a few weeks later to refasten a suture that had come loose and was pressing against his spine. But he did not need to wear the traction halo that time. When the doctors finally declared him healed, they said his neck was as good as new. He would be able to do all the things he had always done. No paralysis, no wheelchair, no limitations whatsoever.

Pat did not forget to thank God for answering her prayer.

Harry came to Pat one day, a few months after the accident.

"Hey, Mom, could we talk?"

"Sure."

"I was thinking I might like to see what it's like to live on my own. Well, not fully on my own. Dino says I can live with him at his mom's house, if it's okay with you. You wouldn't need to pay for it or anything."

Harry move out! She had just thanked God for sparing him, and now she was going to lose him anyway. But this was different. "Are you unhappy here?"

"Oh, it's not that. I love being with you and the guys, but I'm eighteen now. Time to try something new."

Pat had moved out of her mother's home when she had been only seventeen. Harry was a year older than that. Still, it felt different from this side of the generation gap. "I'd sure miss having you around. But I guess you are getting older."

"So you wouldn't mind?"

"No, I won't mind. I'll just bawl my eyes out for the next year and a half!"

"Thanks, Mom. I'll bawl too, as long as I can go."

Pat's nieces and nephews had been growing up as fast as her own boys had. Still, it was a bit of a shock when Mary's daughter Becky called to announce that she had gotten engaged. Becky was going to get married? Well, she wasn't a child anymore—she was a year older than Harry, after all.

"When's the happy day?" asked Pat.

"Sometime in the end of September."

"Well, that will give us just enough time for the wedding shower. You will let me throw your shower?" It was not a question, but a statement.

"Yeah, sure. That would be great."

Pat liked any kind of party, but wedding showers were especially cheerful. Her mind was already rolling with ideas. Where would she hold it? Should it have a theme? What about food, and door prizes, and games?

That Saturday, she went to the annual bazaar held at the church hall. The bazaar was an interesting cross between a craft show and a rummage sale. You could always find some-thing there that you didn't know you needed until you saw it.

As she walked along the aisles in the main room, she was struck by the layout of the place. It would be the ideal place to hold the wedding shower! There were plenty of tables, a good-sized kitchen, and bathrooms that somebody else kept clean. She would definitely have to find out how much it would cost to rent the hall.

Then her eyes were drawn to a plaque lying on the table in front of her. It was a little poster glued onto a wooden block. Across the face of the poster were printed all the words of Psalm 23. Along with the now-familiar verse about God being with us through the Valley of the Shadow of Death, there were other verses: about God leading us to green pas-tures and still waters; about Him restoring our souls and leading us in righteousness; about being blessed in front of our enemies; and about how we can live with Him forever. Pat had to have that plaque! She paid the quarter, or dollar, or whatever it was, and clutched the plaque tightly, as if carrying a briefcase full of top-secret documents.

When Pat got home, she read the psalm repeatedly, thinking long on the words printed there. She understood less than half of them—but she was drawn to all of them. "Surely goodness and mercy shall follow me all the days of my life: and I will dwell in the house of the LORD for ever." *Goodness and mercy? Forever? Amazing.*

She took down the landscape that hung in the living room and hung the psalm in its place. It looked like it belonged there.

The next week she called the parish secretary and found out that not only was the hall available several Saturdays in September, but it was also reasonably priced. She decided to skip any of the flashier themes like Hawaiian luau or Tuscan festival and went with the more traditional umbrellas and swans. She bought lots of white and silver ribbon, tablecloths, invitations, and food, tons of food. She invited all the women on Becky's invitation list, fifty in all. Then she turned her attention to the preparations. Food for fifty women was going to take a while.

Oh! And what about a door prize? There has to be a door prize. Pat's eyes wandered around the living room as she tried to imagine what she should get for a door prize. Her eyes lit upon the basket of yarn beside her chair. A partially completed afghan was draped carefully over the basket. *An afghan! I could make a nice big one—in autumn colors. And I could tell the women to bring little kitchen gadgets to use as tickets. For every gadget they bring, they will get one chance at the afghan. Ooh! That'll be perfect!*

She was so busy with her preparations that September presented itself almost before she was ready. The food was warming in the oven at the church hall, and the place looked splendid. The guests arrived in a cheerful mood, each one exchanging one, two, sometimes three or four or ten, little gifts for chances at the afghan. Pat had not expected this. She had set but a single, empty laundry basket beside the sign-in table to receive the incoming trinkets, but the women brought so many gadgets she had to send across the street for two additional baskets. By the time she had gathered in everyone's offerings, Pat had collected three overflowing baskets of kitchen doodads.

The shower was a success. The women all had a good time, Becky's future sister-in-law became the proud owner of a gorgeous new afghan, and Becky had enough wooden spoons to keep a houseful of miscreant children quaking in their sneakers for years to come.

As she was tearing down decorations and cleaning up leftover food, she got to thinking about Suzzane. She was about Becky's age, just a couple of years younger. She could be dating already. Then Pat had a dreadful thought. What if her daughter inadvertently went out with one of her own brothers? Either Harry or Brian could conceivably ask out a girl Suzzane's age. Oh, that would be awful! Pat consoled herself with knowing that *Suzzane* wasn't a very common name. If either of the boys brought home a Suzzane, then it would be time to worry.

What does Suzzane look like now? she wondered. Was she blonde like she had been at birth? Or had her hair darkened over the years like the boys? *I bet she's beautiful,* thought Pat.

Pat's mood fell as she thought about these things, remembering the past and imagining what might have been. She had ended up meeting Pete so soon after the adoption, she probably could have kept Suzzane after all. It made her cry to think about it.

It was even worse on the day of the wedding. Seeing Becky, radiantly happy in her white gown and veil, standing beside her parents, only drove home the reminder that

Pat also could have been a mother-of-the-bride. Now it would never be.

Pat walked up to Mary. "Everything is absolutely beautiful. You must be so proud."

"Honestly, Pat, everything's happened so fast, I haven't had time to adjust to it."

Just then, a slender man, maybe twenty or so, dressed in a plain, white gown, entered the sanctuary from one of the side rooms and began to light the candles. He struck Pat as odd, too young to be a priest, but too old to be an altar boy.

"What's with the overgrown altar boy?" she asked Mary.

"That's Jack Marshall. He's the new deacon."

"I didn't know deacons served as altar boys."

"They don't always, but Jack is about Becky's age, and they know each other through the youth group, so she asked him to serve instead of getting altar boys."

"Live and learn," said Pat. All the deacons she remembered were high and lofty creatures, almost as distant as priests. This one looked like a regular guy. And they called him Jack—just plain old Jack. Things certainly had changed since she had been a girl.

"He's quite good-looking."

Mary gave her a look that told what she thought of her sister's irreverent remark and went off to join Dave. It was just about time for the service to start.

The wedding was beautiful. And Pat, who always cried at weddings, cried at this one for a reason that no one there knew about. Suzzane.

chapter 12

A few years after the wedding, Kevin got a remarkable offer from his boss, who had acquired a partially-finished rental home in one of the better suburbs north of the city. Kevin could live there rent-free, as long as he kept an eye on the place and did some minor renovations now and then. Of course, Pat and the three younger boys were welcome to come along, though Brian was old enough to be on his own already.

No more midnight sirens, drug deals on the sidewalks, or triple-bolted doors. This neighborhood had class. The men held steady jobs; the women took good care of their homes; and the children spent their days in school, rather than in a detention center. The house itself was upscale too. It even had stained-glass windows on the front wall of the living room. Pat was enamored by the place.

One especially pleasant day, Pat sat out on her porch soaking in the sun and chatting on-and-off with the other idle housewives who had the pleasure of sitting out beside her. The boys were off doing whatever they did these days. They had become so closed lately. Was it because they were up to something they didn't want to tell her about, or was this just how it was with teenage boys? She would have attributed it to school activities, but for the fact that Peter was the only one still in school.

Pat was pulled from her thoughts by the floral delivery truck that had just pulled up in the driveway. What was this all about? It wasn't her birthday, nor any special anniversary. It wasn't even Groundhog Day, so the flowers couldn't be for her.

The delivery man emerged from the truck with a gorgeous bouquet of exquisitely-arranged, fresh flowers and turned toward the women. "Any of you Pat Golwitzer?"

"I am," said Pat.

"Then, I suppose these are for you." The man smiled with delight at Pat's expression as he carried the bouquet up the steps and placed it in her hands. "For the lovely lady."

"Why, thank you," she stammered, as he returned to his truck. Pat opened the attached card and read it: *To Pat, for being such a great friend. Kevin.*

"Who's it from?" asked one of the women.

"Kevin. And it's not even my birthday. He sent them just because."

And that was the way it was for the next two years—just because.

However, happiness can't last forever. Pat knew that better than anyone. So, one day, in the upscale house in the classy neighborhood, her world exploded. Kevin came in from work with a strange, almost-shy look on his face and blurted out the most unexpected thing she could imagine.

"Pat, my boss says I have to choose between you and my job. He says you're not good for me, that you're dragging me down in life. So I need to move out and make a life for myself. We both need to get out of here tonight. I'll drive you to wherever you want to go, but you need to be out by tonight."

Pat couldn't speak. She couldn't even cry, not for a long time. Then she finally said in a tiny, broken voice, "Really?"

Kevin just nodded. He had already said what he meant to say, and there was obviously no need to discuss it. Was this the same guy who had sent her flowers, "just because"? Now he was abandoning her—worse, kicking her out onto the streets—for what? Just because?

He started gathering Pat's belongings from every room in the house and carrying them out to the front lawn. He did it so quietly Pat thought she had fallen asleep and was stuck in a nightmare. Then he packed a few of his own things and threw them into the dump truck that was parked by the curb.

She finally realized Kevin was serious. This was the end. But where would she go? What about the boys? She picked up the phone and began to dial. She didn't even know who she was calling.

"Hello?"

"Hi, Beck." She had dialed her niece Becky. "Kevin kicked me out. I need a place to go. Can I come stay with you and Joe?"

"Whoa, say that again. Kevin kicked you out, and you need a place. Right away?"

"By tonight. He says he'll drive me wherever I want to go."

"Of course you can come here, but what about the boys?"

"Brian practically lives at his buddy's anyway, and Eddie is old enough to join him. They are working on a place for Peter. He's the only one that really needs looking after."

"Would he want to come here too?"

"No, he's fifteen-going-on-twenty and ready to follow after his brothers. Becky, my life is breaking up all around me. One minute life is fine, and the next, we're all out on the streets!"

"You just hang in there, Aunt Pat. It'll work out somehow, and I'm sure your boys will find good places. They are all survivors."

"I hope so."

Kevin dropped off Pat in front of Becky and Joe's house with no more than a suitcase, a box or two of trinkets, and a *Well, it's been nice, Pat. See you around.* Then he drove away.

Becky helped Pat carry her boxes into the house and set them on a chair.

They looked at them awkwardly for a moment. Neither knew quite what to say. Finally, Becky spoke, "You can have the room across from Meghann's." Becky had been married for five years already. Meghann was their three-year-old daughter. "We can unpack later. Let's sit first, and you can tell me about it."

The ladies took seats in the living room. Meghann climbed up beside Pat and cuddled close. Pat smiled at her great-niece and began, "I honestly don't know what happened. Everything was fine between Kevin and me—no fighting, no arguments. Then he comes home and announces out of the blue that I'm a drag on his life, and it's over. He said his boss told him it was me or his job. How could I have been a drag on his life? We weren't even married! He brought in the money; I cooked the food. Not that we were intimate, mind you, but I thought we were the best of friends."

"Oh. That is hard to make sense of. And the boys?"

"They each went to a friend's house. Yesterday, we were a family and today—" Pat's eyes swelled with tears.

"It must be so hard. I know Kevin was a good friend. But your boys are practically grown. Peter is the only one still in school, right?"

Pat nodded and wiped a tear.

"Listen, Aunt Pat, maybe it was just time. Even if Kevin feels the need to move on to other things, you still have your boys, and you can see them any time you want to. So let's talk about you. You need a place to stay and something to do. I called Joe a little while ago, and he said you are to consider this your home. And we will do everything we can to help you figure out where to go from here."

Pat relaxed a bit. This was the same Becky who had fallen asleep on Pat's carpet when she had been a small child, the same niece for whom she had thrown that wonderful wedding shower. Over the years, they had become more than aunt and niece; they were friends.

Pat soon settled into the routine of her new family and decided she wanted to help out a bit. So, when Becky was out running errands with Meghann on a particularly hectic day, Pat decided to make dinner. She looked through the cupboards. There wasn't much there. They definitely didn't have a food budget as big as Kevin's had been. Then she looked in the freezer. Ah, there was something she could work with. Four large chicken breasts—just the thing for herself and her three hosts.

Pat thawed the chicken in the microwave and coated it in her signature blend of flour, salt, and pepper. She knew Becky was especially fond of her fried chicken.

She whipped up some mashed potatoes and canned corn and had it all ready when everyone got home.

"Mmm, this meal is delicious!" exclaimed Joe, his mouth full of mashed potatoes.

"I like the chicken!" added Meghann.

Becky looked like she couldn't quite find words to express her thoughts. Didn't she like fried chicken anymore? Finally, she spoke. "Aunt Pat, this meal is delicious, but you used up all the chicken I had left for the week."

"But there were only four pieces, one for each of us."

"I know, but I normally use one breast for each meal."

"That would make for some mighty small pieces of fried chicken."

"I don't usually make separate pieces of meat for everyone. I take a piece and cut it up real small so it can spread through a whole casserole."

"Oh." Here she had meant to do a nice thing, but she had used up a week's worth of meat. She had been with Kevin for nine-and-a-half years. She had almost forgotten what it was like to pinch pennies. "I'm sorry. I had no idea."

"That's okay. I know you didn't. And you do make the absolute, best fried chicken in the world," Becky said. Still, the rest of the meal felt a bit awkward. It was hard to live in another family's house.

chapter 13

aturday night, Becky invited Pat to come to church with them. "We leave for church at quarter-to-nine in the morning. That way we can catch both Sunday school and the service. If you'd like to come with us, we'd love to have you."

Pat had been thinking a lot about God as she grew older, and the recent breakup of her family had caused her to think about Him even more. She probably wouldn't have ventured to go to church on her own, but going with someone else would be easier. "Sure, I'd like to go."

She met with a dilemma the next morning, though, when she realized that the small collection of personal items she had brought from Kevin's house did not contain anything suitable for church. She told Becky about her problem.

"Oh, the people at Saint Michael's won't mind. You wear whatever you have, and it won't look strange to anyone."

Pat chose her prettiest outfit, a shirt with flowers on a dark background and a pair of black slacks. They didn't look too bad after all.

She felt a bit nervous as they pulled up in front of the impressive Tudor building. The structure was not remarkably large, as city churches go, but its doors were wide open, and she was about to step inside. That was an imposing thought. Her anxiety vanished, though, the minute a friendly couple smiled at her just inside the door.

"Hi, I'm Bob, and this is my wife Carol." Carol smiled and nodded. "Welcome to Saint Michael's. Are you a friend of Joe and Becky's?"

"I'm her aunt. I'm afraid the building will collapse if I step inside; I haven't been to church in years."

"The roof hasn't fallen in yet, and we've had quite a few visitors who haven't been to church in years. You just come right in."

Pat felt at home at St. Michael's. The people were friendly. She felt close to God there too. She understood when the priest explained the Bible in Sunday school. And, during the service, she felt an awe of God that she hadn't felt since she was a child. Pat began to worship God, and it filled a hole she had known was there, but hadn't known how to fill.

Summer moved into autumn, and St. Michael's Episcopal Church began preparations for their Christmas pageant. Pat accompanied Becky and Meghann to practice on Saturday mornings. Meghann was assigned with the other two- and three-year-olds to be little lambs. Their job was to crawl down the aisle bleating an occasional *baaa* now and again. Then they were to sit on the platform, looking as lamb-ish as they could, while the congregation listened to a reading of Luke 2.

Pat had heard portions of that passage before, mostly on Christmas programs on TV, but it was different this time. This wasn't some cute, emotionally-charged cartoon; it was a sacred retelling of a real event—an event that was, she began to realize, more important that any TV show had ever made it out to be. This was about God coming down to rescue mankind. Christmas really seemed different that year.

It was different in other ways too, some very sad ways. For one, Pat didn't have her sons. And, though she did make an effort to keep in touch with them, each boy seemed bent on building his own separate future. She didn't have Kevin either, that man who had become such a good friend and stabilizing force in her life. And she didn't have an income, not even enough to buy little trinkets for Meghann. Staying with Joe and Becky was comfortable in some ways, but they had made it clear they weren't looking for a long-term houseguest. She needed her own life, and for that, she would have to get a job.

Pat found the want ads and turned to the help-wanted section. As always, there were plenty of waitressing jobs open, but she wasn't sure she had the stamina for that sort of thing anymore. There was an opening for a night watchman, but she couldn't picture herself in the uniform. How about a veterinary assistant?

Becky walked in and glanced down at the paper. "You looking for a job?"

"Yeah. It's time I faced things. My life isn't going back the way it was. "

"Anything look promising?"

"There is an ad here for a researcher at Roswell but, somehow, I think they wouldn't be interested in me."

"Probably not. What can you do? I mean, what would you like to do?"

"What I'd like to do is be a secretary. But I don't have the skills. All I've ever really done is wait on tables and sell overpriced junk at parties in the evening."

"You should go to school then, and learn how to be a secretary."

"I'm forty-two years old! You think they'd take me at that age? Not to mention that I'm a high school dropout without a penny to my name."

Becky continued, as if Pat had said something totally irrelevant. "You could get your GED and then apply for financial aid. There's always money for college. You should go for it, Aunt Pat. You're still young and smart. This is your chance to be anything you want to be."

Pat thought all evening about what Becky had said. She was young and smart. She could be anything she wanted to be. Forty-two really wasn't that old, she supposed. Suddenly, she remembered a phone number in her purse. Like a hopeless dream, she had carried it around for over ten years now. She grabbed her purse and pulled the paper from her wallet. It was creased and water-stained, but the writing was still readable: *EOC—Everywoman's Opportunity Center. Call today and start making your dreams come true.* A phone number was written on the bottom of the card. *I wonder if they are still open,* she thought, as she laid the paper carefully on her dresser. She would have to call tomorrow and find out.

"Everywoman's Opportunity Center; this is Delores. How may I help you?"

"Hi. My name is Patricia Golwitzer. I saw your number on TV—oh; it must be ten years ago—and I wrote it down. I've carried it in my purse all this time, never realizing that I would someday need it. I've been out of the workforce for twenty years, and I don't have a diploma. I was wondering if there was anything you could do to help someone like me find a job."

"You have called the right place, Mrs. Golwitzer, because preparing women like you for a productive future is what we are here for. If you like, we can set up a time for you to come down to the center, to take a little test, and register for the program."

"Oh, I don't think I could pass an entrance test."

"It's nothing as grueling as that. We just need to evaluate your current educational level, so we will know best how to steer your course of study."

"I could come down tomorrow, if that would be okay."

"Would ten o'clock suit you?"

"I'm not exactly sure when the bus runs, but I think I could come somewhere around then."

"Wonderful! I'll look forward to meeting you sometime around ten o'clock tomorrow. You have our address, 210 Delaware Avenue?"

"Yes."

"See you tomorrow, then."

Pat was very nervous—an entrance test. Still, she was excited too. Maybe this time her life really was going to turn around.

She caught the earliest bus she could, and made it downtown before nine. That was too early to go in, she thought, so she surveyed the center from outside. It was an old brick building set back from the street. It looked like it might have been a Catholic school or an office building a long time ago. The windows were new, though, as was the sign above the front door. *Everywoman's Opportunity Center*—this was the place all right.

She found a bench by the sidewalk and sat down to wait. Hundreds of people passed by as she sat there, some on foot, most in cars. Did they know this was Pat's big day, the day she was going to head off into a bright, new future? Ah, what was she thinking? Forty-two years old, and she was feeling like a schoolgirl. But she wasn't a schoolgirl. She was sure of that. And there was no way she was going to pass any entrance test.

At quarter-to-ten, Pat could sit still no longer. She got up and headed straight for the door. A well-dressed black woman with an incredibly winsome smile welcomed Pat at the door. "Mrs. Golwitzer?"

"Call me Pat."

The woman held out a welcoming hand. "I'm Delores Skoki, and I'm glad to meet you, Pat. Come on in."

Mrs. Skoki instantly put Pat at ease. She sat there, very calm and dignified, as Pat poured out her life story, crying through most of it. "I'm sorry. I didn't mean to cry. It's just been so hard."

"I understand. That's why we're here. We want to help make things a little less hard for you, Pat. We want to help you prepare for a bright and productive future. The first thing we will need to do is have you take a little achievement test."

Pat smiled. But she wasn't really nervous anymore. "I warned you on the phone; I'm not very good at tests."

"This is the kind of test no one fails."

Pat was surprised at how much she knew. The test wasn't hard at all.

"Well, you don't know yourself as well as you think you do!" said Mrs. Skoki, after she had scored the test. "Most of our clients score below one hundred twenty-five, the minimum score needed to consider taking the GED. You scored over two hundred. You are not only trainable for a job, Pat, but I think you would make an excellent student. Have you ever considered going to college?"

"College! I can't even tell my right foot from my left half the time."

"I'm quite serious. Though you would need to complete the GED as a formality, you are academically ready for college classes."

"I can't believe that. I just came here hoping you could help me find a job—but college?"

"College would offer you more than just a job. It would prepare you for a career." She handed Pat a catalog from the local community college. "Look through this, and see if any of the courses of study look interesting. In the meantime, I'll start enrolling you in our GED class."

Pat scanned the catalog: *Automotive Technology; yeah right. Criminal Justice; too dangerous. Culinary Arts; done enough of that. Dental Hygiene; yuck. Hotel Management; boring. Office Technology . . . Office Technology, could that be it?* Could I really become a secretary after all these years? She hurried up to Mrs. Skoki's desk, almost too afraid to ask, lest her dreams be shattered one more time.

"Um, this listing here for Office Technology and Word Processing, does that mean Secretarial Science?"

"Mmm-hmm."

"And are my scores high enough to get into that program?"

"Oh, absolutely. By the time you get your GED, you'll be ready to make A's in every one of those classes."

"Are you serious? I could become a secretary?"

"Sure you can." Pat's countenance fell with a sudden realization. "What's the matter?" asked Mrs. Skoki.

"I couldn't possibly pay for college. I don't have a job, remember."

Mrs. Skoki smiled. "Oh, that's no problem. You are eligible for enough grants that you could pay for school, bus fare, books . . . maybe even get a little lunch now and then."

Pat was ecstatic. She signed all the necessary papers to be in the GED class and rushed home to tell Becky the good news.

Pat was a natural at school and an asset to the other women at the Center. They sat together at a long, wooden table where they could either focus on their workbooks alone or ask each other for help as they pleased. Pat spent half her time studying, and the other half helping the other women. However, she seldom needed them to help her. Somehow, in her twenty-five years out of high school, Pat had come to understand grammar, current events, algebra, and economics in a way she could not have as a teenager. What she didn't know, she quickly learned. Pat studied at the Center for only three months and passed her GED with high scores. She was a high school graduate at last!

chapter 14

The three campuses of Erie Community College sprawled across the county. The city campus alone was housed in a massive, stone structure that covered an entire city block. Pat stood in the center of the building and looked up at the successive rows of archways stacked one upon another until they met the glass ceiling that allowed sunlight to flood the central courtyard. Classrooms hid behind those arches, several floors of them. Pat was overwhelmed.

She wanted to run back to EOC and hide beneath the table. Why couldn't she just study for her GED with Mrs. Skoki the rest of her life? She eventually found the elevator and took it to the fourth floor. Now she was on the other side of the arches. She walked up to the railing, stood beneath one of the arches, and looked down. The view was magnificent, if you weren't afraid of heights. Someone was standing where she had stood just a few minutes before. He was looking up at the endless arches with the same look of wonder she had worn. It must be his first day too.

Pat found the Department of Office Technology and entered the main office where she was greeted by Gloria Hudson, a very friendly woman who looked to be in her fifties. Mrs. Hudson and Pat hit it off instantly. By the time Pat left her office, she had signed up for her classes, arranged for a position as a work-study student in the Office Technology Department, and made a new friend.

Pat walked into her first class early the following Monday morning. Mrs. Townsend's math class was held, along with most of Pat's classes, on the fourth floor. Other than being old enough to be the mother of her classmates, Pat fit right in. She learned quickly, almost instinctively. Pat knew the answer to almost every problem Mrs. Townsend put on the board. And the problems she didn't know, she quickly figured out.

English class was the same way. So were sociology, and history, and basic computer skills. Pat thrived in the academic environment. She almost wished she could be a student forever.

One afternoon, about halfway through the semester, Pat was doing her work-study shift in the office. "Pat?" asked Mrs. Hudson. "Have you, by any chance, seen the immunizations folder for incoming students? The Health Department thinks it might have accidentally found its way up here in the morning deliveries."

"If it found its way in here," answered Pat, "the Health Department might as well consider it lost forever."

"Yes, well, our files are a bit of a mess, aren't they?"

"Mess is an understatement. They are a disaster. I just hope you don't lose my file before I graduate, or I'll never get out of here."

Mrs. Hudson looked at Pat with sudden inspiration. "What are you working on now?" she asked Pat.

"Updating the grade files from last quarter."

"What would you say if I asked you to pull apart our entire filing system and put it back in a way that makes sense? It would be a good experience for you, and the Department of Office Technology really should have their files in decent order."

"All the files?"

"All the files."

Pat looked at the piles of paper stacked on every cabinet, table, and windowsill in the room. "It will take a few years."

Mrs. Hudson grinned. "You have until next May. That's fourteen months."

"It will keep me busy; that's for sure."

Pat dove into the project with gusto. She spent long hours after classes sorting and shifting and rearranging thousands of misplaced, and often forgotten, forms. Within a month, she had the files organized and all the paperwork in its proper place. Mrs. Hudson was so pleased with Pat's work that she took her out to dinner at a fancy restaurant. Pat felt so proud. The filing had been as *secretarial* as any work she could imagine, and she had done it well. *Move over, Della Street; Pat Golwitzer is on her way!*

When she made the honor roll at the end of her first semester, she was astounded.

Pat soon became one of the regulars on campus; in the library, at the lunch bar, and in the halls. People nodded and greeted her by name. Even Dr. Garner, who usually scowled when people said hello, smiled when he met her in the halls. Pat had found her niche.

Pat loved classes at the college. They were small, and the teachers gave each student a lot of attention. By her fourth semester, she was typing seventy-seven words per minute with ninety-five percent accuracy. She could also

Pat graduated from college in 1990.

run a word processor, use a spreadsheet program, and organize a filing system better than Mrs. Hudson. With A's in almost every class, and the skills needed to be a good secretary in almost any type of office, Pat was finally ready for graduation.

Ma was so proud of her. Her daughter had risen above the stagnant mire of poverty and illiteracy into which she'd been born, and made something of herself! All of Pat's teachers came up and shook Ma's hand at the graduation ceremony. They praised Pat's accomplishments and congratulated Ma on raising such a fine daughter. In a sense, it was a graduation for them both; Pat had become a degreed secretary, and Ma had become the mother of a college graduate.

Still, the degree didn't make Pat a real secretary. Real secretaries have jobs.

"I can get you an application to work at Fedco," said Mary's husband Dave, a few days after graduation.

"The radiator factory?" asked Pat. "A factory wasn't exactly what I had in mind in the way of secretarial jobs."

"The secretaries don't work in the plant," said Dave. "They work with the bosses in the cozy building across the street. Padded chairs, air-conditioning, tinted windows . . . just the sort of place you'd like, Pat."

"Okay, get me an application. I'll give it a try."

Pat was called in for an interview a few days later. It seemed the customer service representative was leaving for a more lucrative position in another company, so they needed someone immediately. Dave had recommended Pat so highly that they hired her on the spot, despite the fact that she had no on-the-job experience.

Before long, she had become so adept at handling the requests of several very large companies that the higher-ups decided to also let her run the brand-new label-making machine. This made Pat responsible for handling clients, processing orders, and printing labels for many thousands of heating and cooling units per day. It was a fast-paced, high-pressure job, and she absolutely loved it.

Pat found it amusing that very little of her job involved typing, filing, or any of the other skills she had learned at ECC. But none of that mattered; she was a secretary, and a good one at that, and she was thriving.

chapter 15

Pat had been at Fedco for almost a year. She found an apartment on the riverfront and had been living on her own for a few months. She felt lonely occasionally, but her job occupied so much of her time that she hardly noticed she was alone. Her boys were adults, living in various sections of the city. She didn't know where Kevin was.

Ma called her one evening with some disturbing news. She needed to have a cataract removed, a minor procedure that no one worried about. However, when she went in to have the routine chest x-ray required of older patients, the doctors had found a suspicious lump in her lung.

Pat tried to calm her mother down over the phone. "Ma, just because you have a lump doesn't mean it's cancer. A lot of things can cause lumps."

"Don't kid yourself, Patsy. I've been smoking cigarettes for over fifty years."

"That doesn't mean you have cancer, Ma. A lot of people smoke, and they don't all have cancer." Who was she trying to fool, Ma or herself? This was the same thing that had happened to her father, and now it was happening to Ma.

"So what's next? Do you need a ride to the doctor or something?"

"No. They took a sample of the lump, and they won't know if it's cancer until Friday. I just thought I'd tell you now, so you know."

"Please call me as soon as you hear something, okay?"

"I will."

As everyone feared, the lump was cancer. Insidious and inoperable. It was just like Dad, all over again. And Suzzane. And Kevin. Was Pat destined to lose everyone she loved?

Ma had chemo, but it made her sick. Within a few months, she changed from a healthy seventy-six-year-old woman to a weak and shriveled patient. When she was too weak to stay at home, she was placed in the residential care unit at the hospital. Pat visited her almost every day.

Her mind-numbing routine of work, visiting Ma, work, visiting Ma, was interrupted in the spring of 1992. It was the day before Easter, and she had gone to see Eddie and Nancy. Pat was reading a book to Michael, Eddie's little boy and her first grandchild, when she received a call from the State Police.

"Mrs. Golwitzer?"

"Yes?"

"Do you have a twenty-one-year-old son named Peter?"

"Yes."

"I'm sorry, Ma'am, but your son has been in a very bad automobile accident. The medical personnel are airlifting him to the County Medical Center. Do you have anyone who could drive you there?"

Pat was dazed. She quickly answered, "No."

"Please stay where you are, Mrs. Golwitzer. We will send someone to drive you. Do not attempt to drive yourself."

"No, I won't." Peter—her baby—in a crash?

"What is it?" asked Eddie.

"Peter. He is being airlifted. They said to stay here."

"Who said to stay here? Where is he being taken? We can take you there." Eddie was a man of action. He didn't like the idea of sitting still when he could do something.

"They told me they'd come and get me. I'd better call Mary."

Pat called Mary often; she had the number memorized. "Hi, Mar? Peter's been in a bad accident. Can you meet me at the hospital?"

"Sure, Pat. Is he going to be okay?"

"I don't know. The trooper just said they were airlifting him, and they were coming to pick me up. Oh, Mary, it's bad; I just know it is."

"You don't know that, Pat. They airlift people for a lot of reasons. You just go on to the hospital, and we'll meet you there."

Mary and Dave were waiting for Pat at the door to the Emergency Department.

"Hurry, Pat. They're waiting for you to see him before they take him to surgery."

"Is it bad, Mary? Oh, I don't want to see him if it's bad." Pat felt faint. A nurse supported her under the arm.

"I think you should come see him, Mrs. Golwitzer. If he doesn't make it, you'll be glad you did." Pat nearly passed out.

"Come on, Pat, let's go." Mary's voice gave strength to Pat. She took a step. Then another.

Pat did not recognize the body on the table as being her son's. His face was all smashed. His limbs were mangled. He looked like something from a slaughterhouse.

Pat stumbled. The nurse and Dave helped her to a chair in the waiting area. They stayed for the several hours Peter was in surgery.

Finally, the surgeon came into the room and walked over to Pat. "Mrs. Golwitzer?"

"Yes."

"Your son has made it through surgery, but he gave us quite a run for it. We've set his arm and put two pins in his leg. The most serious injury is the blow to his head. We won't know the effects of that for several days, after the swelling goes down.

"He will be heavily sedated for the next few days. You can see him now, if you like, but after that, I recommend you go home and get some rest. We will call you immediately if there is any change."

Dave and Mary accompanied Pat to where Peter lay in the recovery room. Pat still did not recognize him. Only the name on his bracelet identified him as her son.

"Come on, Pat," said Mary. "You can stay at our place tonight. I gave the nurse our number. Tomorrow is Easter. The best thing we can do for Peter right now is to get some rest, and then to go to church and pray for him."

Pat followed numbly.

There were only a few hours left in the night. Pat lay on Mary's couch, exhausted, but she couldn't sleep. *God! You take everyone I love! Isn't Ma enough? She's old. I can understand You wanting to take her. But Peter? What good could it possibly do to take him? It makes no sense!*

The sun arose on Pat's questions, but it brought no answers.

The familiar smells at St. Michael's, and the soft glow of the candles, worked together to calm her soul. This was a holy place. God was here. No matter what else was going on in Pat's life, she always felt better when she came in here.

St. Michael's was an Episcopal Church, which like Anglican churches around the world, used the Book of Common Prayer as a guide to the service. The book is a collection of beautiful prayers written by men hundreds of years ago. Pat had heard these prayers so many times in the years she had attended St. Michael's that she could recite them on autopilot, even as her mind was actively thinking of something else.

This morning she was, of course, thinking of Peter. Actually, she was wrestling with God—struggling to beg from Him the life of her son, even as she was trying to surrender to His will. The voice of the priest broke into her wrestling, and joined her mental conversation like a voice from some other reality. He was reciting the Nicene Creed:

. . . *On the third day He rose again . . . and He shall come again in glory . . .*

The part of her mind that knew the prayer by heart, understood that the Creed was referring to Jesus, the One who died and rose again. But the part that was struggling with God heard a different message. It heard a promise, as if from Heaven: *Pat, your son will be okay. I will not take him yet.*

Chills ran up and down her spine, and her hair stood on end. She had never heard from God before. She had entreated Him. She had thanked Him. She had even yelled at Him at times. But she had never heard Him speak to her—until now.

chapter 16

P eter got better. Ma didn't. She slipped into a coma, then woke just long enough to call for a priest, and to beg God to forgive her sins and to receive her soul into Heaven. Then she died.

The loss of her mother was more painful than anything Pat had ever experienced. She was filled with regret for all the times she had been impatient, and guilt for the times she had been harsh. She would do anything to have her mother back! How could she live with this big, aching hole?

There was no funeral planned for Ma. She, like Dad, had donated her body to medical research. The remains wouldn't be available for at least a year, and they would be nothing more than ashes by then. Pat longed for some sort of memorial service and the closure it would bring.

She was at Mary's, the afternoon after Ma's passing, when Becky came in after a day of teaching at the local Christian school.

"Our principal, Mrs. Adams, feels awful about us not having a memorial service. When I told her how Grandma didn't have a church, she said we could hold a service there at the school, if we wanted to. Pastor George from the Chapel even offered to come and give a little devotional, if we want. She told me to check with you guys to see if you wanted a memorial service. If you do, I am to call her back, and she'll handle it from there."

Pat looked at Mary. "What do you think?"

Mary gave a small nod. "Let me call everyone."

Mary called her brother and sisters. Most of them had wanted some kind of service, but they all attended different churches. A school would be a nice, neutral place to hold it. As for Pastor George, he was the perfect choice. Being the assistant pastor at a non-denominational church, he would be respected by the mixture of Catholics, Episcopalians, and Mormons in the crowd. Becky called Mrs. Adams. She said she would make all the arrangements for a gathering in the cafeteria that Friday morning. What a blessing.

The sky was overcast and drizzling on Friday morning. How fitting. Pat looked in her closet. She hadn't thought about her wardrobe before. Should she wear black? Or was that just for funerals? This was a memorial service; she would wear purple instead.

She met Eddie and Jane in the school parking lot, along with her sisters Janet, Carol, Helen, and their families. Dave and Mary pulled in shortly after. So glad to see one another, they hugged and shed a few tears before composing themselves to go inside.

They found the cafeteria filled with people: neighbors, friends, and long-forgotten acquaintances who had come to comfort Pat and her siblings. Somehow, Mrs. Adams had arranged to have the service announced in the paper. She was so thoughtful.

Pastor George waited until the reunion chatter subsided before beginning the devotional.

"Perhaps the most difficult days are those when we face the loss of a loved one. When that person is your mother or grandmother the pain is especially acute. But God shares our sorrow, and He offers us comfort.

"Most of you are probably familiar with the twenty-third psalm." Pat's heart leapt within her. How did he know? "It compares God to a shepherd who cares for His sheep."

The Lord is my shepherd; I shall not want.
He maketh me to lie down in green pastures:
He leadeth me beside the still waters.
He restoreth my soul:
He leadeth me in the paths of righteousness for his name's
*   sake.*
Yea, though I walk through the valley of the shadow of death,
I will fear no evil: for thou art with me;
Thy rod and thy staff they comfort me.
Thou preparest a table before me in the presence of mine
*   enemies: Thou anointest my head with oil;*
My cup runneth over.
Surely goodness and mercy shall follow me all the days of
*   my life: and I will dwell in the house of the Lord*
*   forever.*

The minister went on to invite everyone in the room to follow the Great Shepherd all the days of their lives, so that they, too, could dwell in His house forever.

Pat's soul was warmed and comforted. Every time she had read that psalm in the past, she had always been struck by how often we must go through the Valley of the Shadow of Death. But Pastor George put the words in a new light. It wasn't just about surviving the trials here in this life, but about following God all the days of our lives—on into eternity—to where there is no valley, and goodness and mercy will never disappear!

There wasn't much more to the service, just a prayer or two and a short eulogy, but it was enough. Pat felt soothed and comforted and restored.

Folks stayed around for a long while, reminiscing and catching up on one another's lives. Pat enjoyed all the visiting.

Then she noticed Mary standing in a corner with a few people from St. Michael's. It looked like she was about to cry, so Pat walked over.

"I can't believe you would let her hold the service here!" one of the group was saying sharply. "Both you and Pat belong to St. Michael's; you should have held it there. She is only a granddaughter. She had a lot of nerve taking things upon herself."

Mary burst into tears. "She didn't take things upon herself," she exclaimed. "They offered to do it."

"Who offered to do what?" asked Pat.

"Oh, nothing. We were just saying how out of place Becky was in holding the memorial service here. Both you and Mary are members of St. Michael's. She should have let you hold it there."

Pat was livid. "Neither Mary nor Becky forced anyone to do anything!" she said fiercely. "The people here offered to provide a memorial service, and they made all the arrangements. It's more than any of you did! Come on, Mary." She reached for her sister's arm and pulled her away from the confrontation.

"You forget everything they said, Mary," Pat said, seething. "They're just rude and jealous. And they certainly aren't acting like Christians. I'll tell you what, if that's the kind of people that go to St. Michael's, then I won't be going there anymore."

Mary dried her eyes on her sleeve. "Not everyone at St. Michael's is like that. It's just them."

"Well, don't bother looking for me on Sunday; I'll find some real Christians, or not go to church all."

Sunday came, and Pat stayed home. She felt a bit uncomfortable about it, so she said a few prayers and sang a hymn as well as she could from memory. The next Sunday was the same. So was the next and the next, until Pat had forgotten the hymn altogether and read the sale ads instead of praying.

chapter 17

Pat threw herself into her work. She had become, essentially, the entire customer service department. She dealt personally with the owners of some large companies such as Modine, Four Seasons, and Advance Auto Parts. It wasn't a surprise when her boss, Patrick O'Conner, came into her office and asked if she'd like to go along on a fishing trip Fedco had arranged for one of its top customers.

"Yeah," explained Patrick, "Shirley from Suprex is coming alone—guess her husband couldn't make it this time—and she wants to go fishing. I'm sure she'll have a lot more fun with another woman along. Any chance you could come?"

"Twist my arm."

"Good. It's supposed to be hot tomorrow, so you might want to bring a hat. Other than that, we've got you covered."

Patrick wasn't kidding. The fishing boat was more like what Pat would have called a ship. It had a full deck above and another below. A giant canopy covered a good portion of the upper deck and made her hat unnecessary.

She had just settled in on a comfortable deck chair beside Shirley when Patrick came up and asked, "Can I get you ladies anything?"

"A pound of fifties," answered Pat.

"Sorry, we're fresh out of those. Would a Coke do?"

"Make it a Pepsi, and you're on."

He turned to Shirley. "And you?"

"Diet Sprite?"

"Coming right up."

As Patrick turned to leave, Pat added, "With plenty of ice."

"Gotcha."

She leaned back in her chair and grinned at Shirley. "I could get used to this."

When the boat reached the deep water, the crew began to set up the fishing gear. Pat laughed when she saw them hang "her" pole off the end of the boat, while she sat back and began the next chapter in her book. She looked at Shirley, who was watching the gulls feed on the flotsam dotting the surface of the waves, and asked, "Have you done this before?"

"I've gone a few times with my husband Hal. He likes to fish. I go along for the ride. I love the water."

"Me too. Though I don't get to go out on a boat much."

Their conversation was interrupted by a shout from the crew. "Fish on line!"

"Come on, Shirley," called Patrick. "It's your line."

Shirley shrugged, then got up and walked over to reel in the fish "she" had caught. It was a twenty-five-pound king salmon.

"Way to go!" said Patrick, when the fish was on board and the crew had taken it below to clean. Shirley gave a little toss of her shoulders and replied with a grin, "It's all in the wrist action."

When Shirley sat back down, she leaned over and whispered to Pat, "I hate salmon, but I don't want to ruin their day."

A few hours later, after most of the others had reeled in a catch, the call came again, "Fish on line!"

"Come on, Shirley, you got another one!"

"Oh, one is enough for me." She looked at Pat. "Why don't you go pull in this one?"

Pat found that it was harder than it had looked from her lounge chair. This fish was a fighter! After much coaching and cheering, she finally pulled in a twelve-pound ocean perch. Patrick had captured the entire event on video. He turned the camera straight onto her face and asked, "Pat, do you know what you just did?"

"Yeah," she sobbed. "I just killed a fish."

Everyone laughed. It was a triumphant ending to a successful expedition.

A few months later, she returned home from work to find a message on her answering machine. It was from the adoption registry network, stating that they might have located her child. Pat would have to wait until morning to return the call.

Suzzane. She would be about thirty by now. What was she like? Pat was thirty years older too. What would Suzzane think of her? Pat had trouble sleeping that night.

She called as soon as the registry office opened. "Hello. National Adoption Registry Network. How can I help you?"

"Hi, my name is Patricia Golwitzer. I have a message on my machine that you might have found my daughter."

"Just a moment." The phone was silent a few seconds. Then the voice resumed. "Yes, Mrs. Golwitzer. We have a contact here from a Barbara Golwitzer, who was given up for adoption in 1963. Her father is listed as one Peter Golwitzer. Is there any chance you could be her mother?"

Pat's heart sank. Suzzane wasn't born until 1966. Pete had mentioned that his surviving child, a girl, had been taken from her mother by the courts and given to a foster family. Barbara must be that child. Pat wiped her eyes and cleared her throat.

"No, I'm sorry. The dates are wrong. Barbara couldn't be my daughter. I was married to her father at one time, though. I suppose that would make my boys her half-brothers."

"Would you mind if Barbara contacted you? She is trying to contact any of her past relatives who can be found. She would be very interested in knowing she has brothers."

"Yeah, sure. Give her my number."

Barbara called Pat a few days after that. Barbara was thrilled to find she had brothers; but Pat was left with a freshly opened wound.

Thoughts of Suzzane dogged her at the most unexpected times: at work, in the store, whenever she saw a fleecy-headed newborn. But, Suzzane was no longer a newborn. She was a thirty-year-old woman. Pat could have stood right behind her in the checkout aisle, and neither of them would have known the difference.

She began watching "The Locator" on TV every evening. It was about separated family members who were trying to find one another. Sometimes they found each other, and sometimes they didn't. The show always made Pat cry, but she watched it anyway.

chapter 18

Many of Pat's nieces and nephews had moved to other states. Carol's son Mike lived near D.C., and Ed's daughter Cheryl lived in Atlanta. Two of Mary's daughters, Rhonda and Becky, had moved as well, the first to Memphis and the second to the Shenandoah Valley in Virginia. Pat decided it was time to make a trip to see them all. She chose as her traveling companions two ten-year-old boys, each of whom was named Michael. One was her own grandson, Eddie's boy. The other was Mary's grandson.

It was interesting traveling with two Michaels. When she would tell one to pull out the map, the other would reach for it. And when she would ask one of them to read her a road sign, both would respond. Before the boys forgot who they were, she decided to call her own grandson Michael, and Mary's, Mike. The system had its flaws, however, as she called Mike, Michael, and Michael, Mike, as often as she got them straight. Still, it made her feel better to think she knew which was which.

The comedy of errors could not help but increase when they arrived at their first destination, the home of her nephew who, unfortunately, went by the popular name of Mike. Of course, it was easy for her to get everyone's attention. All she had to do was yell, "Mike!" and three fellows would run to her assistance.

Mike—big Mike, that is—lived with a darling woman named Vicki. The two of them had set up a trampoline in the backyard, reportedly for the use of their grandchildren. However, big Mike spent so much time out there with his young visitors that Pat couldn't help wondering if the trampoline was not really for him.

"Pat, would you mind calling the guys for supper?" asked Vicki, the second evening they were there.

"Sure." Pat stood at the door that faced the backyard and called, "Mike!"

"Yes?"

"Yes?"

"Yes?"

She could hear them all giggling. "Oh, you quit it and come in for supper."

After everyone had finished eating, big Mike, whom the boys affectionately called Uncle Mike, built a fire in the fire ring. They sat around it on lawn chairs and talked long into the evening.

"Have you ever seen the President?" asked Mary's Mike, who loved history and government and reading the signs at historic landmarks.

"No," answered Uncle Mike. "Washington's a big place, and we're really not that close to the city. But there's a really neat place in D.C., called the mall. It's not a shopping mall, but a big park where they have all the monuments. It's a mile long; isn't it, Vicki?"

"Something like that."

"Anyway, in the middle of it is the Washington Monument. It looks like a giant needle sticking up into the air."

"Is it near the White House?"

"I think it's right across the street. When you come next time, maybe we could take you there."

"I wish we didn't have to leave tomorrow," said Pat's Michael. "Can't we stay another day?"

"Not unless you want to miss out on the rest of the trip," answered Pat, though she shared his feelings. Mike and Vicki's house was so relaxing—no alarm clock, no business clothes. And, as much as she liked her job, it was good to get away for a while.

Despite their melancholy feelings from the night before, Pat and the two Mikes were excited when they hopped into the car the next morning. They were heading for the Great Smokey Mountains. Pat could have gone south on the Piedmont and then swung up into Atlanta, and so avoided the mountains altogether, but she wanted the boys to see them. Besides, she had planned a surprise.

"A train!" the boys yelled as they got out of the car a few hours later. "Hey, Mike, check out the wheels. They've got that bar thing between them."

"It's a steam engine," said Pat, "and it will take us right through the mountains."

She wasn't kidding. They were going to ride an old steam engine that ran through a tunnel which had been cut straight through the mountains. The boys were excited when they saw the mouth of the tunnel rapidly filling their vision, but as they sped farther and farther into it, and the spot of daylight shrank behind them, they grew afraid.

"Whoa!" shouted Pat's Michael, when the track took them around a curve that completely cut off their view of the entrance behind them. Neither could they see an exit up ahead. Other than the tiny light that shone upon the tracks from the front of the engine, they were completely in the dark.

Everyone in the passenger car grew silent, almost as if trying to hear the darkness that surrounded them. Then, as suddenly as they had been closed in, a dot appeared up ahead and grew until it became a recognizable archway. They finally understood why *seeing light at the end of the tunnel* was such a good thing.

The train ride was a round-trip affair, designed to give tourists a taste of what it had been like to travel long ago. After a lunch at the end of the line and a trip back through the tunnel—it wasn't nearly as scary this time—they got back in the car to complete the journey to Atlanta.

That portion of the trip sped by. Two days at Cheryl's—which was as wonderful and as hard to leave as Uncle Mike's—followed by a few days more with Rhonda's family in Memphis, and they were headed back to Virginia to stay at Becky's for a week.

Becky and Joe now had four children: Meghann, and her three brothers Colin, Evan, and Nathan. Colin was ten, just like the two Mikes, so the three boys hit it off like old friends, which they were.

The boys had played together at holidays and family reunions for the first eight years of their life. It was only in the last two years, since Joe and Becky had moved their family to Virginia to join a conservative Mennonite church, that the boys had been separated. Those two years were no barrier to the boys, however. Within a few minutes, they were as absorbed in one another as if they had never been apart. Pat hardly noticed the boys after that. There was no need. There were more adventures to be had in and around Joe's country home than three cousins could accomplish in one short week.

Pat, meanwhile, pulled up a chair and a footstool and enjoyed the easygoing hospitality at Joe's. Becky made all the meals; the children made the messes; and Joe kept them all entertained.

"Don't suppose you'd be up to a game of Scrabble?" Becky asked after supper.

"I haven't played Scrabble in years! I probably couldn't even spell my own name right."

Pat and Becky set up the game on the kitchen table while Joe went out to play football with the boys.

"What were you thinking you'd like to do while you were here? D.C., the caverns, a picnic up at the lake?"

"All of them." Pat laughed. "Let's start with the caverns. I think they would love that. And the boys mentioned wanting to go to D.C. I wouldn't mind seeing it myself. But I don't think I'd be up to all the walking."

"I think they have tour buses that go around to all the sites. You can get on or off whenever you want."

"Are they air-conditioned? I'm dripping with sweat," Pat said, as she wiped her hand across her forehead.

"They're open air; I think."

"Let's do the caverns tomorrow, and save Washington for next week."

"Okay," said Becky. "And what about Sunday? It's been quite a while since we went to St. Michael's together—what, fourteen, fifteen years?"

"Something like that. I haven't been there since they lit into your mother at Ma's memorial service. I just couldn't stand how they treated her."

"You haven't gone to any church since then?"

"Well, here and there, occasionally, but nothing long-term. I'd like to go on Sunday, but I wouldn't have anything to wear." Pat looked down at her own slacks and top and then at Becky's homemade, calico dress.

"You would just wear what you have on. Mennonites dress like this, but we don't expect others to. People will love you just as you are."

"Are you sure?"

"I'm sure."

Pat was relieved. She really did like the idea of getting back to church. It had been so long. And here was a chance to go with Becky again. Just like old times.

chapter 19

Pat was nervous on Sunday morning. She was no longer afraid the roof would collapse when she walked into the church building, but Mennonites were so different. She would stick out like a sore thumb.

Twenty or so cars were parked in the gravel parking lot that wrapped around the tiny white building. A humble sign on the lawn read *Bethany Mennonite Church, Everyone Welcome*. People greeted each other and talked as they made their way up the cement steps and through the plain, wooden doorway. Pat was struck by the number of children—many more than there had been at St. Michael's—and they were so well-behaved!

"Well, who do we have here?" asked a smiling man, extending a hand to Pat as she walked across the parking lot with Joe and Becky.

"Pat Golwitzer."

"Well, hello. I'm Clair Heatwole. Good to see you." Then there was a flock of other greeters. Clair's wife

Dianne, and Raymond and Elizabeth Ann Shenk, and Allen and Faye Good, and Vivian Benner, and . . . she could not possibly keep up with all the names.

The inside of the building was like no other church Pat had ever seen—or even imagined. It was just a simple room with paneling on the lower half and white-painted drywall above that. There was no crucifix anywhere, not even a plain, flat cross. There were no pictures, no candles. Even the podium was unadorned, just a plain, wooden lectern suitable for holding a Bible and a few notes. She felt as if she had entered a time warp!

Even more remarkable were the people. The men—all dressed in plain dark suits and white shirts with no ties—sat in the ten or so benches on the right side of the room with a few of the children, and the women in their calico dresses and head caps sat on the left side with the rest of the children. That was it.

The service began when a man got up from somewhere in the middle of the church and walked to the front with a song book. He led a couple of songs that Pat didn't recognize. That was okay, though. She wouldn't have been able to sing along even if she did recognize them; there was no organ to help her know what notes to sing.

She liked Sunday school, though. The children and men all left the room and the ladies were left by themselves. That was nice. Their teacher was one of the women who had shaken Pat's hand as they came in, but Pat couldn't remember her name. This was nothing like Sunday school at St. Michael's where the priest had taught and they had all listened. There was a lot more sharing among the ladies here. She got the feeling that many of them had studied the lesson ahead of time. And they knew their Bibles! And yet, for all they obviously knew, they didn't make Pat feel stupid.

After Sunday school, a man who looked identical to all the others got up to preach. Wait! She knew who he was. He was Clair Heat—something or other, the man who had said hello to her when she had first gotten out of the car. He was the preacher? Why, he looked just like everybody else. And he hadn't put a *Father* or *Reverend* in front of his name when he had introduced himself. Whew! This church sure was different.

Pat was absolutely captivated by Clair's sermon. He talked so excitedly about how wonderful Jesus is. *Preeminent* was the word he used.

It was only a sermon. And that was it. Oh, there had been a few more songs and a prayer or two, but they had been regular prayers—the kind you pray yourself— nothing like the beautiful, prewritten prayers she had heard each week at St. Michael's. For all that simplicity, and despite the absence of candles and priests and fancy prayers, Pat felt close to God. For the first time in many years, she had worshiped with other people. It felt so wonderful.

When the service was over, Clair's wife Dianne came and asked if Becky and everyone who was with her could come over for lunch. That would be nine guests! Pat half hoped Becky would decline the invitation. She had a lot to process already. At the same time, she loved being with these people. They were so warm and inviting. Becky checked with Joe, who said he loved the idea of spending the afternoon with Clair's family.

The Heatwoles lived on a sprawling dairy farm not far from the church. This was a great delight to the Mikes, neither of whom had ever visited a real working farm.

"You'd think she was expecting us," whispered Pat to Becky when she saw all the food Dianne had prepared. Salisbury steak in mushroom gravy, real macaroni and cheese, green beans in some sort of creamy sauce, and broccoli and raisin salad.

"She was, in a way. All the ladies at church take turns being the hostess. They make enough food to feed whatever company might show up on Sunday. It's Dianne's turn to be hostess, and you're company. Joe and I just have the privilege of coming along. So glad you're here, Aunt Pat," Becky said with a twinkle.

"Remind me to be company next time I come," Pat replied.

The meal was as delicious as it looked. After the meal was over, Dianne shooed the men and children out of the kitchen so she could clean up from the meal. Becky and Meghann got up to help her.

"So, this is your first time down here?" asked Dianne. Her Virginia accent was adorned with just the sweetest tinge of a drawl.

"First time to Becky's. It's absolutely beautiful here! I don't know how you can stand it."

Dianne smiled. "Oh, we like it pretty good."

"Have you always lived on a farm?" asked Pat.

"Clair has. My father was a businessman. But our children have grown up here. I'm afraid they wouldn't know how to do anything else."

"And I wouldn't know the first thing about milking cows."

"Becky says you are in charge of the ordering department at a radiator factory?"

"More like customer service, but, yeah. I'm not really in charge, though; I just do all the work." Pat smiled.

"That must be so interesting."

"I like it. But it's not like here. I can't believe how nice everyone here is!"

"Are they not nice back home?"

"They're not mean or anything. But, it's not the same. The people here seem to sincerely like you, no matter where you come from."

"Well, we sincerely like you, Aunt Pat, and we hope you come to visit us often."

Pat enjoyed the way Dianne called her *Aunt* Pat. Becky had introduced her that way, and Dianne had just kind of picked up on it. *Aunt Pat.* It sounded nice, almost like they were all family. Pat had even forgotten she was a stranger, until she caught a glimpse of herself in the bathroom mirror.

Faye called the next day to invite Becky and Pat to come over for lunch. Of course, the children were invited too. The meal was as delicious as Dianne's had been. When it was over, and the children had run outside to explore, Faye said, "Just leave the dishes. I've got a little something planned for us out in the sunroom."

The little room off the kitchen was, indeed, a sunroom, and the bright, warm light that flooded in from the windows gave it a cheerful feel. Screens in the windows let in a soft breeze. A table in the corner of the room was covered with an assortment of homemade papers and dried flowers.

"Take a seat wherever you like," Faye said. She sat down beside them. "I thought we could make a wall hanging. But you can make whatever you like."

Pat looked at the supplies laid out before her. "These flowers are gorgeous! Did you make them?"

"Oh, they're just some flowers from my garden. They're not as pretty as the ones you get in the store."

The three women spent the next two hours gluing dried flowers into attractive arrangements on card stock. Of course, they talked the entire time. Pat was struck by how sweet and kind Faye was. Like Dianne, she treated Pat like an old friend. Surely, she had other things to do than to entertain a stranger for an entire afternoon. And she wouldn't take any money for the supplies!

When they got back to Becky's house, they found some ripe, ready-to-eat tomatoes sitting on the porch. With them was a note that read: *Becky and company, I thought you would enjoy these. Love, Elizabeth Ann.*

Pat lay awake a long time that night. She didn't want the day to end. She thought about Dianne, and Faye, and

Elizabeth Ann. *These people are wonderful. I can see why Joe and Becky like it here.*

The week flew by. Each day seemed better than the one before, and before she could blink, it was time to go home. At least Pat had one more place to take the boys, or leaving Virginia—and the people there—would have been too hard.

After warm hugs and tears on many faces, Pat and the Mikes packed into the car and headed for Ohio. She had not told them where they were going. She had saved that to cheer up their sad departure.

"You guys ready to head home?" she asked when they got to the end of Joe and Becky's road.

"No-o-o-o!" they said in unison.

"Then what would you say about a stop at the Football Hall of Fame?"

"For real?" came the equally loud, but much happier, response.

Pat loved driving. It did not tire her at all to drive eight hours to the museum, tour it for a couple of hours, and drive another five or six hours home. The Mikes were great company and, as long as she had them with her, driving was a pleasant end to a wonderful vacation.

Pat liked football as much as the boys did. Watching them enjoy themselves made the side trip even more worth the drive. Still she couldn't help but feel that the museum wasn't as fun as it would have been had she never been to Virginia. It was as if she had left a part of her heart behind with Joe and Becky and their wonderfully strange people, and she would not be truly content until she could be with them all again.

chapter 20

Age crept up on Pat like a tiger. Then it pounced. Her doctor had been warning her for some time that she was headed for both diabetes and heart disease, but it was hard to take the warnings seriously when she felt so good. Oh, she tried the diabetes diets, but they were boring and unrealistic. The heart diets were worse. She did switch from Pepsi to Diet Coke, though. She found that the taste of the two colas was so similar that she could at least give up one source of sugar without having to give up soda altogether. However, there were no good substitutes for cookies, candies, steak, and ice cream.

Pat was in for her regular physical one day when her diet collided head-on with her DNA. She was having her blood pressure taken in three different postures: first lying down, then sitting, then standing. When the doctor saw that Pat's blood pressure dropped fifty points between the three positions, she called an ambulance to take Pat to the hospital immediately.

While she waited for the ambulance, Pat called Harry. They had moved into a duplex shortly after she started work at Fedco. Harry had taken the upper flat and Pat the lower. They had dinner together almost every day. It was so good to be with him again. "Hi, hon. I'm at Dr. McGorry's office. Listen. She wants me to have a minor procedure to prevent further problems with my arteries. But she won't let me drive myself to the hospital, so I need to ride in the ambulance. I'll probably be in until tomorrow, but I didn't want you to worry when I'm not home at the usual time. I also need you to have one of your buddies drive you here to the office so you can pick up my car and drive it home. I'll leave the keys at the front desk here. Just be sure to get them by three."

"Do you need me to meet you at the hospital?" Harry sounded concerned.

"No, there's no need. It would probably be all over by the time you got there. I might call for a ride home tomorrow, though."

"I'll be here."

Pat had been very careful not to tell Harry how serious things were. He was quite squeamish about all things medical and would have been torn between his desire to be there for his mother and his dread of hospitals. So Pat was left to face a frightening procedure alone. *Perhaps I should call Mary,* she thought. Then she thought better of it. There was no need to alarm her sister either. This surgery was going to be a little nothing; a whiff of anesthesia, a quick opening of the artery, a tiny mesh tube, and a few stitches.

No, there was no reason to get Mary all worked up. Still, it would have been nice to have someone to distract her while she waited.

Pat was prepped and lying on a narrow bed in pre-op when an almost-familiar face peeked around the curtain. It was one of the hospital volunteers; Pat could tell by her vest. Pat had the feeling they had met before.

"Hi, Pat. Mind if I come in?" The visitor must have seen the puzzled look on Pat's face, because she said, "It's me, Yolanda—Rey's wife."

Of course! Rey Rodriguez from Fedco. Yolanda was his wife. Pat had met her a few times at company picnics and Christmas parties.

"Yolanda. I'm sorry; my mind is a bit scrambled right now."

"Mine would be too. I saw your name on the incoming list, so I thought I'd come up and keep you company. Would you like me to stay, or would you rather be left alone?"

"I'd love company! Sitting here with nothing but my own thoughts is terrifying."

Yolanda was a natural visitor. She talked about everything except Pat's upcoming procedure. Before Pat knew it, she was in the operating room, and they were putting a mask on her face.

The surgery went fine, and Pat went home the next day. She had to have a stent put in another artery a few years later, and it, too, was uneventful. However, Pat wasn't done with doctors. Even though her arteries were now opened wide, she had developed another problem with her heart.

It was more of a problem with her nervous system, but it involved the heart. It was called neuro-cardiogenic syncope, and it caused her to pass out when she stood too long, or under certain conditions. Fortunately, all she had to do to treat the faintness was to sit or lie down. Life certainly was getting interesting. Still, nothing was so serious that Pat couldn't work around it—until the day she and Harry went to get the car out of the shop.

She had been having some trouble with the transmission. Fortunately, it was still covered by the warranty. When the mechanic handed Pat the invoice and said, "Sign here," she picked up the pen and began to sign her name. She wrote the *P,* then the *a,* but all she could get out of the pen after that was a string of *a's.* She was stuttering with a pen! It made no sense. She knew how to spell her name, P-a-t-r-i-c-i-a G-o-l-w-i-t-z-e-r, but all that came out when she tried to write was *Paaaa . . .* which trailed off into a faint scribble.

Doctor McGorry suspected immediately that Pat had suffered a stroke, and she ran tests to confirm it. Sure enough, Pat had experienced a temporary loss of blood-flow to the part of her brain responsible for writing. It was probably due to the same type of blockage that had caused her to require stents in her coronary arteries.

"Pat," said the doctor, "I'm sorry, but you are already taking all the medicines available for someone with your type of problem. The rest is up to you. A low-cholesterol, low-carbohydrate diet and more exercise might help, but the combination of coronary artery disease, diabetes, syncope, and now a stroke, is getting to be too much for you to handle. I think it is time you considered leaving work."

"You mean for good?"

"Yes."

"I could never afford it. I'm not eligible for Social Security for at least five years!"

"You would be eligible for State Disability and probably supplemental Social Security as well. You might not get quite as much as you make now, but I don't think you have much of a choice."

Pat went to Fedco to talk to her boss. "My doctor says I had a stroke. She said that with my combination of health problems, I should go on permanent disability."

He looked sympathetic. "Pat, you know how much we depend on you. You are practically our entire customer service department. But it won't do anyone any good if you have a heart attack, or something worse. As much as we'll miss you, you need to do what the doctor says. And, listen, I'm pretty sure you got in on the company disability plan when you first came on board. Check with Sue, though. She can tell you for sure."

Pat did have the company's extra disability insurance. With it, added to the state's disability coverage, her income wouldn't change that much, at least for the next five years.

Fedco threw a farewell party for Pat. It pleased her to know they appreciated her. Still, it didn't make the final good-bye any easier. When the party was over, she grabbed the last few items off her desk, turned in her key, and drove out of the parking lot for the last time. Pat's career as a secretary was over.

chapter 21

Pat enjoyed her first day of retirement. The second
and third days were kind of refreshing too. By day
four, though, she decided she didn't really like the
idea of being independently wealthy. She was bored, a
little depressed, and stiff from too many hours in front of
the TV. She decided it would be a good time to visit Joe
and Becky again.

She had been there several times since that trip with the
Mikes, and each trip only intensified her desire to return.
She always had a great time with Joe's family.

"Hey, Beck," she said into the phone. "Would you like
some company?"

"You know I would."

"Since I'm retired now, I can stay longer. Would a month
be too long?"

"You know better than to ask. When are you thinking of
coming?"

"How about Saturday?"

"Perfect. I should tell you, though; we have revival meetings next week. That's when a traveling preacher comes and gives special sermons. We will be at church every night for a week. You can either come with us or stay home, your pleasure."

"No problem."

When Pat exited the interstate and turned into Mennonite country, she felt like she was coming home. It didn't matter that she was neither a Mennonite nor a country girl. There was something comforting in the smell of hay, the clip-clop of passing horses, and the whir of the buggy wheels that followed at their heels. Yep, Pat was coming home.

She drove on past the poultry plant—phew! that was a smell she didn't miss—and crossed the little bridge over Dry River. *I wonder why they call it that? There's always plenty of water in it.* As she passed Faye's house, she remembered the afternoon that she and Becky had spent making dried flower pictures in the sunroom . . . and the evening when they had all gathered in the garage to shell soybeans. What a time that was! She never could quite figure out how popping slimy beans into a pail held between your knees could be so much fun. But that's the way it was down here. The most ordinary things seemed to produce the best memories.

As the road narrowed into a gravel lane, then disappeared into the river, Pat suddenly realized she had gotten herself turned around. She wasn't exactly lost; she just didn't know where she was. That was another thing about this place. Few of the roads were straight, and the idea of a grid did not seem to have occurred to anyone. There was even a place where Mt. Clinton Pike intersected with Mt. Clinton Pike! Folks explained that it wasn't really an intersection of two roads, but rather just a really sharp turn. Sharp turn, nothing! The first Mt. Clinton was the leg of a *T*, and the other Mt. Clinton was one of the arms. The other arm, which was, to her mind, the continuation of the Mt. Clinton arm, had a totally different name. So, if someone was traveling along the Mt. Clinton arm, they would have to make a ninety-degree turn to stay on the road. The unsuspecting traveler who navigated by logic would never realize that by going straight he had just turned onto another road!

So, here she was, with her front wheels in the river and her back wheels on a road that, for all she knew, was probably also named Mt. Clinton. One thing was sure; she couldn't go forward. She backed up to the last intersection which was, not surprisingly, the corner of West Dry River and West Dry River.

Pat worked her way back to the main road, reminiscing at all the familiar places she passed: Ralph's woods up on the hill, the Old Order church, the flower-covered wall, and Silver Lake. She marked the patch of grass where she and Becky had parked their lawn chairs, while Joe took the boys out on the rubber raft. The boys were still young enough, then, to believe that snapping turtles could bite sinkholes in the side of a boat. One of them was so convinced of an impending attack that he wouldn't even step into the craft until Joe tethered it to such short a line that it could do little more than slap against the shore. Not that Silver Lake could be said to have a shore. It wasn't even really a lake—more like a pond. There weren't any real lakes down here, so folks just dammed up streams and dug out little ditches and called them lakes. Still, Silver Lake was a lovely place.

Pat finally pulled into Joe's drive with a sigh of satisfaction. That last hour had been the best part of the trip.

"You made it!" said Becky as she and her aunt shared a big hug. "How was your trip?"

"Piece of cake."

Pat woke the next morning refreshed and in good spirits. It was Sunday, and she would be going to church. She never had found a church of her own since that blowout at Ma's memorial service, but she always went to Bethany Mennonite when she came down here. The strangeness of the little white building with no cross or candles had worn off a long time ago.

"Hello, Aunt Pat!" said Elizabeth Ann, almost before Pat got out of the car. "It's so good to see you again." The greetings were the same from everyone else, warm, enthusiastic, real. Pat basked in the glow.

"How long can you stay?" asked Clair, shaking her hand after church.

"Just a month."

"Is that all! You'll be here for revival meetings then, won't you?"

"I'm hoping to come every night."

"Well, good. We'll be looking forward to it."

She knew preachers were expected to say things like that. But she also knew Clair really meant it. And it wasn't just because he thought everyone should go to his church. He just wished her the best and, in all his imagination, he couldn't think of anything better to wish for her than that she could join them that evening.

After lunch at a friend's house and a quick nap, Pat found Clair greeting her again. "Well, Aunt Pat, are you ready for some soul-stirring preaching of the Word?"

"I think so."

"Good. Good. Andy Coblentz will be preaching. I think we're in for a good time tonight."

Pat listened attentively. Clair was right; Andy was a soul-stirring preacher. What he said about the two roads troubled her, though. Something about the road to Heaven being so narrow that only a few people would find it especially bothered her. *Who are the few?* she wondered. Then Andy said something that made her heart shudder, and he read it straight out of the Bible. Some people who are on the road to Hell think they are really on their way to Heaven, but when they approach Jesus in the end, He will say that He doesn't know them. *How horrible! What if that's me!*

Pat didn't say much on the ride home. After the children had gone off to bed, she sat down at the table with Becky.

"Can I ask you a question?" she said in a soft, almost tremulous, voice.

"Sure."

"Those people at church, do they think I'm not a Christian?"

Becky did not answer immediately. She looked puzzled, almost sad. "There are a lot of meanings for the word *Christian*. They would certainly think you are a kind of Christian, in the sense that you are not Muslim or Jewish. But they would probably say that you are not following Jesus the way He wants you to. So in that sense, I guess, you wouldn't be a Christian."

"What do you think?"

"Oh, Aunt Pat, I'm not the one to judge who's a Christian and who's not."

"But you believe like they do." Pat looked at Becky with earnestness, her eyes begging for an answer and fearing what it might be.

"Yes, I believe like they do. If I had to, I would say that you are not that kind of Christian."

"So, what about the two roads? Am I one of those that Jesus will say He never knew?"

"I can't say who Jesus knows. The Bible does say that only those who love God with their whole heart, and really try to follow what He teaches, will be on that narrow road. I fear there will be a lot of American Christians who find out too late that they have been walking on a different road than they think they are."

"I've always considered myself a Christian. I mean I don't worship another god or anything."

"Do you love Him with your whole heart as much as you are able? Is He the most important thing to you?"

"I want Him to be. But I'd be lying if I said that I've always lived like He wants me to." Pat felt her eyes watering. She had never talked about her faith so candidly. It was hard. "I want to be that kind of Christian, and I want to live the right way—the way God wants me to—the way you all do."

Becky seemed unsure of what to say next. "Are you saying you just want to live better," she paused, "or are you saying you want to join Bethany, or what?"

Pat knew how much hinged on her answer, how much she would really be saying if she said she wanted to join a Mennonite church. Then she did one of the hardest things she ever remembered doing. She nodded her head. Everything else was easy after that. "All of it. I want to live like God wants me to. And I want to join the church. And, yeah, I want to become a Mennonite. Beck, my life up to this point has been a waste. It seems like nothing I've done has turned out right, and something inside wants to change."

"Oh, Aunt Pat, that's wonderful!" Becky came over to Pat's side of the table and gave her a long, deep hug. They both cried a little, but neither was at all sad.

"So," said Pat, when they had composed themselves and were seated across from one another again, "what's next? I mean, I can't exactly join a church that's five hundred miles from home."

"I suppose not. But Joe and I were thinking anyway. We don't think it's a good idea for you to live alone since the stroke. What if you needed help or something?"

"Harry's right there."

"I know, but he's at work. Joe and I thought that since we have so much room here, you might want to come and live with us. It seemed like a good idea before tonight but, now that you want to join the church, it seems perfect."

"No." Pat looked down, uneasy. "I know it sounds good, but you guys asked me to move out once before. I don't think I could stand going through that again."

"It was different then. You weren't sick. It was what we all needed then. We needed our space as a family and you needed to move on with your life. But it's different now."

"I don't know. You said I could stay the last time too."

"I promise, Aunt Pat. We won't kick you out."

Pat was silent for a while. "As long as I have your word."

"You have my word."

"All right then. I'll come." Pat smiled softly. Then she rested her head in her hands and made a sound that expressed something between laughter and surprise. "Whew! This is all so fast!"

"I know. It's exciting. I never imagined you'd want to become a Mennonite."

"You know what it was? Everybody else pressured me to come to their church, and they told me how I should be good. But you guys never did that. I've been coming down here for—what—six years? And all you did was show me love and acceptance. You never told me to change, you just welcomed me and loved me, and that made me want to change without you saying anything."

The two women laughed. It was hard to imagine any group wanting to take in either one of them!

Then they planned. They could talk to Clair tomorrow and make all the arrangements for Pat to begin instruction classes. She could permanently take over Evan's room. Of course she'd need to go home to get her things, but since she would be downsizing to one room, that shouldn't be too hard. As for clothes—clothes? Why, she would need a whole new wardrobe! She'd be one odd-looking Mennonite in slacks and a top. Oh, she could worry about that later.

The rest of the vacation (or should she call it a *pre-move?*) flew by. The flurry of arrangements, coupled with the details that needed to be worked out with the ministry, seemed to shrink the days, and before she knew it, the month was over.

"Don't you worry," called Becky from the porch. "You just get together a few things, close out your accounts, and we'll make all the arrangements on this side."

Pat's smile was bigger than it had been when she had arrived four short weeks before. She had to leave for a while, but she'd be back. And she'd never have to leave home again.

chapter 22

P at looked at the mess scattered all over the house. You'd think being limited to only a room's worth of possessions would have made packing easier, but the opposite was true. Rather than flinging everything into miscellaneous boxes, she had to sort every item in the house, one tiny piece at a time, to be sure she chose only those things that were dearest or most necessary.

She had already decided to abandon things like dishes, furniture, cookbooks, and knickknacks; Becky had plenty of those already. But, that certain picture, or that one small memento, those were the things that were precious. To find them, she had to root through every drawer, shelf, and cupboard in the house. She even searched in the couch cushions; there was no telling what treasure had been hidden there by some well-meaning or careless little fingers.

"Don't worry about the mess, Ma," said Harry. "I'll clean it up after you're gone. Just get the things you need and leave the rest." Harry hadn't said much about Pat's move.

She wondered how he really felt. They had been sharing the same duplex for over ten years, and her move was bound to affect him. Yet all he said was, "You go for it, Ma. A person's got to do what he's got to do." And that was all.

She would certainly miss him. He was her oldest, and he had been beside her through most of the changes in her life. If only he could retire too. Oh, well, they would have to find a way to be satisfied with visits on holidays, like other people.

The telephone broke into her thoughts. It was Becky.

"Hi, Aunt Pat. I have some news. First off, I want to tell you that it will not at all affect our plans to have you move in with us, but we are planning to move to West Virginia."

"You're what?!"

"Well, the Mission Committee from church called and asked if we would move to a community in the mountains. I guess one of the churches back there is really small, and they could use more people. We told them we would move as soon as we could find a place."

"I don't know what to say. I mean, I pictured moving to Bethany where I know everybody."

"I know. It's kind of strange to think of going somewhere where we don't know anyone. But I'm sure those people are as nice as the ones here."

Pat didn't speak for a moment. "What about my instruction class? and my baptism? Would I drive back and forth to Virginia for meetings?"

"No, Clair said the ministers in West Virginia will take over your classes after we move."

"Oh."

"You still want to come?"

"I've got nothing to keep me here."

"Yeah, that's what I thought. Besides, it'll be fun to go on a new adventure together."

"That's one way to look at it."

Pat was shaken by the call. She knew all the people at Bethany. Who knew what the ones in the new church were like? It was hard to believe they could be as warm and accepting as the folks she already knew. She couldn't help but think of Psalm 23 . . . *He leadeth me in the paths of righteousness for His name's sake. Well, God, this isn't exactly the path I thought I would be walking on. I'm not sure I'm up to this.*

It did not take Joe and Becky long to find a home in the mountains. It was big enough for Pat to have her own room without any of the boys feeling crowded. They planned for a closing date in mid-August. That would give her plenty of time to complete her affairs and be ready the day Joe came to get her things.

Joe and Becky both came to get Pat on moving day. They loaded her few things into the van and headed to their new home. So much was new and strange. She was moving to a strange place, to live among people she had never met. It wasn't that she wanted to stay where she was, but she wasn't sure she wanted to go forward either. She just wanted the world to stop spinning for a while.

Pat had never been to West Virginia, but she fell in love with the wild and wonderful state when she first tipped over the peak of Shenandoah Mountain and gazed into the breathtaking land beyond. Ridge upon ridge stretched into the mist at the edge of the horizon, all of it blanketed by a thick coating of green. There was not a single town to mar the beauty of the hills. Pat felt like she was on the top of the world looking down into an endless forest. She wondered where, in all of that paradise, her new home was.

As they descended the western side of the mountain, they were swallowed up by the never-ending hills. Hill, then valley, then gap; hill, then valley, then gap; and on it went for a full hour and a half. Sometimes, when they drove along the gorge between two ridges, Pat felt like she was disappearing into a forest that was frozen in time. The forest was so enchanting, though, getting lost in it seemed like a pleasant ending to a long and wearisome journey.

She was mesmerized by the stream that ran along beside the road. Born of the springs that bubbled from rocky outcrops in the hills, the water ran ever downhill, gurgling and dancing as it went. Pat heard it singing through the open car window. She was struck by a childlike wish to splash her feet in its shady pools.

Then there were the leaves, and the sunlight sparkling through them, and the indescribable smell of life! They all beckoned to her. Pat was enthralled.

Eventually, they turned onto a narrow, gravel lane which ran into the woods and wound itself up the side of a hill. There, with a view of both the sun's rise and its set, was the loveliest little home she could imagine. It was a long, doublewide trailer with a deck on both the front and the back. A few small sheds dotted the property, but other than that, the house had an unobstructed view.

A big moving van containing all of Joe and Becky's belongings arrived just behind them and, with it, a crew of smiling, hardworking people who were every bit as friendly as those Pat had known in Virginia. Yep, this was the same kind of Mennonite, all right. In less than two hours, they unpacked everything and set the house in good order. They even made the beds.

After the work was done, everyone met on the front lawn for a picnic. The church ladies had made all sorts of picnic foods: sandwiches, potato salad, cold fruit salad thickened with tapioca, cookies, bars, and mint tea. They sat in the evening breeze, eating off of paper plates and getting to know one another.

Pat was too exhausted to visit very long. She quietly snuck off to her bedroom to rest (or was it to hide?). She was just untying her sneakers when three men knocked on her open door.

"May we come in?"

Pat wasn't sure who they were, any more than any of the other strangers with whom she had spent the last few hours, but she gave the expected response and welcomed them in. The men did not introduce themselves. They acted as if they thought she knew who they were. Perhaps she had met them earlier, but with all the back-and-forth of so many people, she wasn't sure she could remember her own name at that point.

"So you want to become a Mennonite," said the oldest of the three. He appeared to be in charge.

"Yes."

"Do you have a living, growing relationship with God?"

No one had ever asked her a question like that before. "I love God, if that's what you mean, and I want to love Him more. I'm not exactly sure what you mean by a living relationship, though."

"We'll go over all that in your instruction classes. Wendell, here, will probably be the one to take you through them." He pointed to the shorter of the two men beside him. He did look a bit familiar. She remembered being struck by how effortlessly he carried heavy boxes and furniture.

Pat nodded. "Okay."

"Do you have any questions we could answer for you right now?"

"Not that I can think of."

"Very well, then." He smiled broadly and held out his hand. "Welcome to West Virginia. May God bless you with a good night's sleep and a close walk with Him all the days after that." The other two men followed up with their own well-wishes and exited the room, leaving a rather amazed woman to ponder the strange chances of life.

chapter 23

Snow came early to the mountains that year. Pat was wary of driving on the winding mountain roads, but she was not about to miss her instruction class. Fortunately, Wendell and his wife Laura lived right on her lane, around the ridge and up to the top of an adjoining hill. It wasn't a bad drive, if she was going fast by the time she reached the bottom of the hill. The lane was icy tonight, though, and she was afraid of slipping into the steep gully to her right. Going fast was not an option.

She hugged the left side of the lane, lightly scraping the car against the mossy bank and sleeping rhododendron bushes that grew there. That gave her a good six feet of clearance. At least visibility wasn't a problem. The snow had already fallen from the sky and the moon shone brightly on low-hanging branches.

Pat saw Wendell's hill up ahead. She accelerated as much as she dared but was still going only ten miles per hour when she reached the bottom of the hill. The car began to climb, five feet, ten feet, fifteen; but for each foot forward, the car decelerated: ten miles per hour, seven miles per hour, four, one. The car stopped. Then it began to slide, simultaneously moving both backward and to the right. The gully waited like a gaping maw.

Pat slammed her foot on the brake. The car kept sliding. She stepped on the gas. The wheels only spun as they continued their relentless creep toward the edge of the lane. Terrified, Pat stomped both feet hard upon the brake. One white-knuckled hand clutched the steering wheel while the other frantically sounded the horn. The right wheel grabbed hold of a patch of grass, and the car came to a tenuous rest.

Pat was afraid to get out of the car. To do so, she would have to remove her feet from the brake pedal. With a mix of panic and prayers to the God she was so lately coming to know as a very real person, Pat continued sounding the horn and flashing the headlights. She knew she was too far from the house for Wendell or Laura to hear the horn, but maybe the lights would reflect off the snow. *Oh, God, help! Please let Wendell look out and see my lights!*

She sat frozen in her seat, afraid lest any small movement would break the equilibrium that held the car to the tiny strip of grass on the side of the road.

Then she saw a light glinting on the trees ahead. The light grew brighter as it bounced its way over the ridge and began to descend the hill. It was Wendell!

The beam from the flashlight lit up his neighborly grin. "Hi, Aunt Pat. Are you having a little trouble getting up the hill?"

"A little trouble! I'm about to slide off the side of the cliff!"

He opened the door and helped her to get out. Then he hopped in as if he had no fear of sliding anywhere, effortlessly pulled the car back onto the gravel, and backed it to the bottom of the hill. "Come on," he called. "You get in, and I'll drive you up."

Laura was standing in the open doorway, light streaming out around her from the warm room behind. "Are you okay, Aunt Pat?" She embraced Pat and welcomed her into the house.

"I almost killed myself down there! If Wendell hadn't come to get me, I don't know what I would have done."

"We saw your light coming up the hill, and then it started going backwards. I told Wendell he had better go check on you. We figured you were sliding down the lane."

"Not just down the lane! I was all the way onto the grass. I don't know what kept me from going over. I was afraid to breathe!"

Wendell chimed in, still wearing the boyish grin that made him so endearing. "The Lord was looking out for you."

"And we're sure glad He did," said Laura. "Come on in to the table, and I'll get you a nice hot cup of tea."

Laura set a steaming pot of tea and three cups on the table that marked the boundary between the kitchen and the living room. Each sat down and took out their copy of *Basic Bible Studies* by W. Heatwole. It was the workbook used by many Mennonite churches to instruct new members.

They had been studying together for a couple of hours, when Wendell looked at page 38 and asked, "How did Adam's fall into sin affect your life?"

Pat read the answer she had written a few days before, "It made it so that I was born wanting to sin."

"That's right," said Wendell. "The Bible says we are born with a sin nature—that our most righteous deeds are like filthy rags compared to what God expects from us."

"Is that why, no matter how hard I try to do right, I always end up messing things up somehow?"

"Yes, but the story doesn't end there. God has provided a way to deal with our sin problem. He sent Jesus to die and rise again so that we could have His righteousness to replace the sin in our lives. What's more, He promises to give us the power to go on and live a righteous life."

Pat looked confused.

Wendell continued, "It will make more sense after you do the next lesson. It's about Jesus and what His death and resurrection mean for us. See if you can finish pages 38 to 45 before next Tuesday."

Pat completed the entire lesson in the time requested—as she did with the other nineteen lessons and by the end of the course, she felt like she really knew what it meant to follow God—to love Him with her whole heart and to trust Him to change her from the inside out. By December, she was ready to commit to being a faithful member of the Boyer Hill Mennonite Church.

She was also ready to be baptized. Though she had been baptized as a newborn, the ceremony had meant nothing to her. It had been more an expression of her parents' faith than of her own. She was an adult now, and she wanted to proclaim to the whole world that she wanted to be the kind of Christian who followed Jesus on the narrow road.

The tiny parking lot at Boyer Hill was filled the evening of the baptism. Not only were the thirty-some members of Boyer Hill there, but more than half of the folks from Bethany had come to support her. All of her old friends were there: Clair and Dianne, Faye, Elizabeth Ann, Vivian, and all the others she had come to love on her trips to Virginia. To think, they had driven two hours just to come to her baptism!

Pat sat on the front bench where everyone could stare at her. She was so nervous. She had chosen to have the baptism ceremony at the beginning of the service so she could get over the hard part and concentrate on the sermon afterward.

Pat stood to give her testimony. "I felt something when I first came to Bethany—the way everyone loved me and didn't care about my past. I thought that was how God was, so kind and forgiving. And when I came here and found the people were the same way, I was convinced that this is how I wanted to be too. I want to love God with my whole heart and love people the way you all do. And I want to live in a way that is pleasing to God. I am sorry for all my sins and thank God for cleansing me. And I ask God and you to help me walk on the narrow road."

Larry Showalter, the West Virginia bishop, approached her bench. Wendell walked behind him with a bowl of water. Pat knew Larry well now, but she thought back to the tall stranger who had introduced himself the day she moved to West Virginia and asked if she had a growing relationship with the living God. She now understood what he had meant by that question. Her relationship with God had grown intensely vibrant during the past few months, and she wanted nothing more than to follow Him for the rest of her life!

Larry asked Pat a series of formal questions about her beliefs. With her answers, she renounced Satan and all his works, repented of her sins, and confessed Jesus as her living and all-sufficient Saviour.

Wendell lifted the bowl of water, and Pat bowed her head over it as Larry scooped up three handfuls of water and successively poured them on her head, saying, "I baptize you in the name of the Father . . . and of the Son . . . and of the Holy Spirit."

Tears of joy mingled with the baptismal waters that dripped from Pat's radiant face. She looked up at Larry. He smiled down at her the way she had always imagined a father would smile upon a child he loved. She smiled in return, then sat down with a feeling of contentment such as she had never known before. God loved her. The church loved her, and she loved them all in return. If a heart could burst from joy, Pat's was about to explode and shower everyone in the room with the love she knew she couldn't possibly contain.

chapter 24

Boyer Hill nestled in one of those outcroppings of civilization that dot the Appalachian Highlands. The land surrounding it was claimed by the forest. Pat felt as if she had been asked to live in the most beautiful place on earth.

Birds she had seen only in books came to the feeder on the deck: goldfinches, titmice, nuthatches, hummingbirds, even a pileated woodpecker! Deer grazed by the side of the road. Raccoons, opossums, even black bears could be spotted by anyone willing to sit in the right place long enough.

"You're one of the few people who doesn't have to talk when they drive," Pat said to Becky as they drove over Cheat Mountain on their way to the grocery store, fifty miles away.

"I like to concentrate on my driving. Besides, the scenery is so beautiful, I'd rather look than talk."

"I'm the same way. It's hard to believe this is what it looks like to go shopping!" She swept her hand across the horizon. "Mountains, trees, and gorgeous views of the sky. Sure beats traffic and garbage all over the place."

"Mmm-hmm."

They rode the rest of the way in silence, except when they passed "the pretty place," on the western side of Cheat. It was at the spot where two forks of the mountain came together to form a sort of corner. A stream ran down the center of the corner with sides so steep that, in places, the water fell in a picturesque cascade. They always pulled over and rolled down the windows when they reached the pretty place.

"It's running full today," said Becky.

"Beautiful!" Pat couldn't explain why she didn't tire of that spot. It was something about the way the water was always changing, yet was always the same. And the gurgling, rushing sound was almost like laughter. It was a delight just to sit there and *be*.

The two of them went to town a couple of times a month, and they always went to the same stores: Walmart and Save-a-Lot. Both stores had motorized wheelchairs so Pat could do her own shopping without worrying about fainting if the syncope hit her suddenly.

Of course, the motorized cart baskets had a twenty-five-pound grocery limit so Pat had to get rather creative when she gathered her merchandise. One gallon of milk (eight pounds), a package of hamburger (five pounds), a case of Diet Coke (twelve pounds)—oops! Already at the weight limit! Better put the soda under her feet. And on it went, with items going into the cart and being pulled back out as

Pat worked around the weight limit. By the time she found her way to the register, she was usually buried beneath so many layers of potato chips, paper towels, and black forest ham that she couldn't reach her change purse.

Pat caught up with Becky in the cereal aisle. "Am I ever glad I found you," she said, her face barely visible amid the items meticulously balanced on the floor, arms, and basket of the cart. "Here, can you grab some of this?"

"Well, if it isn't a talking shopping cart." Becky relieved Pat of the topmost strata of groceries. "You think you can use all this in the next month?"

"I needed to get a few things for my trip."

"A few things?! You think you'll fit all that on just one bus?"

"Ha, ha. I don't know if I'll be able to get to a store." Pat was planning to visit Carla, a good friend from Fedco, who had recently retired and moved to Slidell, Louisiana.

"Are you getting excited?"

"Yeah, a bit nervous, though. I've never traveled by bus before."

"I think you'll like it. You can get up and walk around, sleep when you want—"

"And I don't have to wait for the next rest stop." They both laughed.

Pat found two new dresses waiting on the counter when she got home. Both were polyester and wrinkle-free. Wendell and Laura's daughter Malinda had made seven dresses for her already, and each one fit better than the last. Pat was so glad for Malinda. She couldn't imagine making all those dresses by herself, but Malinda whipped them off almost effortlessly.

Pat tried on the first dress and looked in the mirror. It was a Kelly-green cape dress, cut in the style worn by Mennonites across the country. It was simple, practical, and modest. Pat felt like a real lady in it—a real, modest lady.

The other dress, an orange gingham, was just as lovely. She was glad to have them in time for her trip. They would travel well. Pat opened her suitcase and carefully packed the two dresses. She would save them for Louisiana.

The next morning was Sunday, the highlight of her week. Pat grabbed hold of the handrail and pulled herself up into Joe's van. The arthritis in her knees had been getting worse lately. Stepping up was becoming especially hard. Sitting too long could be painful too, but stepping up was excruciating.

By the time they got to church, the pain was gone. She was grateful for that. She followed Joe and Becky into the foyer and smiled to see her pastor James Helmuth already there. She liked James so much. His sermons were down-to-earth and easy for her to understand. Visiting ministers sometimes came to give the sermon, and she liked them too, but she was always glad when it was James's turn.

The service at Boyer Hill was very much like it had been at Bethany: a few songs, Sunday school, some announcements, and the sermon. When James got up to preach, Pat pricked up her ears.

"I brought along a little model for today's message. It's of Jesus and the two thieves." James pulled a wood sculpture from a shelf beneath the pulpit and set it where everyone could see it. It was of three plain crosses, each fashioned from pieces of wood that were curved to resemble the arms and posture of a man. The first cross bent downward, as if bowed in sorrow. The middle, and largest one, had its head and arms lifted toward Heaven. The third was a smaller, but no less joyful, copy of the second. James pointed to each cross in turn.

"This first cross is the man who railed on Jesus. Though he was facing his own death, he didn't have the sense to worship his Creator.

"The second cross is Jesus, looking up to the joy that was set before Him.

"This last one is the man who accepted Jesus. He is looking up because that very day he would be with Jesus in paradise."

Pat hurried to shake James's hand after the service was over. "I like the way you used that little wood carving to illustrate your point. It makes so much sense the way you said it. I couldn't help but want to be the third man. He was so happy with his face and arms turned to the sky. Only a fool would want to be the first man."

"It makes you wonder how so many people can reject Jesus. All I can figure is they don't know what's in store," James answered. His eyes moistened as he spoke of those who ignore or reject Jesus. Pat loved that about James, the way he cared about people. It wasn't just words with him; he really cared.

chapter 25

at followed Brenda to the car after church. Brenda opened the front door and ushered Pat into the front passenger's seat. Then she hopped into the backseat of the Trailblazer and scooted to the middle before her sons got to the car. Richard and Kendrick were now both taller than she.

"I feel funny about you sitting back there," Pat said to Brenda. "Not to mention driving me all the way to your place, letting me spend the night, and then driving me to the bus station in the morning!"

"Oh, Aunt Pat, don't give it a second thought. We practically live right across from the station."

James and the boys joined them a few minutes later.

"You comfortable over there, Aunt Pat?" asked James.

"Very."

"Do you get carsick easy?"

"No."

"Are you sure?" Now why was James grinning like that?

"I've never gotten carsick in my entire life!"

"Well, these hills can turn your stomach mighty quick, so you just tell me if you start to feel a little green around the gills."

Pat smiled at the image of herself with gills. "I'll be fine."

Pat was fine—until somewhere on the west side of North Mountain. Whether it was the excitement of going on a trip, or the nervousness of riding a bus across country by herself, or if it was James's constant questioning about the current state of her well-being, Pat's gills did, indeed, start to turn green.

"Pull over," she shouted suddenly, and in a tone that told James she meant *now!*

She got out of the car just in time to toss her breakfast over the guardrail. Her gills felt better after that, though her cheeks were decidedly redder.

Brenda put an arm around Pat's shoulder and held out a water bottle. "Would you like some water?"

"Thanks." Pat opened the bottle and rinsed out her mouth. "I feel like a fool."

"Nonsense," said Brenda. "Don't you think a thing about it. These curves make us all queasy at times."

Pat really did feel better, and the rest of the drive wasn't too bad. She even perked up enough to give James a friendly jibe. "Now I will honestly be able to tell people that my pastor makes me sick!"

Pat spent the rest of the day trying hard to convince everyone that she was fine. The Helmuths, in turn, spent it making sure that she was. They fussed and hovered over her like a mother over a child with a fever. After assuring themselves that their guest had truly suffered from nothing more than a passing bout of motion sickness, they left her to fall asleep. The last things she noticed, as she drifted into a restful slumber, were the homey smells of fresh sheets and aromatic candles.

The next morning, after a home-cooked breakfast and all the warm feelings that went with it, Pat said good-bye to her beloved pastor and his family, and boarded the bus.

The bus crept along. Pat had imagined they would move much faster than this. There were so many towns and small stations to stop at, that they no sooner got up to speed than they had to slow down again. In some of the towns, they never got up to speed at all.

Pat pulled a new novel from her bag and reclined in her seat. She had finished her last book just an hour ago. Normally, she liked to let one story settle in a bit before she started another one, but they were passing through an industrial section of a medium-sized city, and the view wasn't terribly inspiring.

She looked at the cover of the book, *Circle of Love,* by Romaine Stauffer. She was not familiar with the author, but Laura's mother Ellen had loaned it to her for the trip. The book had more than three hundred fifty pages; she ought to get a few good hours out of it.

Pat was quickly absorbed in the story of a young man who had rejected his good upbringing to marry a woman who did not really love him. It was such a sad story. He had the kind of family anyone would dream of, but he threw it all away for a phony love. *I sure know what that's like!* she thought.

By mid-afternoon, they broke into open country and sped up considerably. She could still see mountains to the west. They were her mountains, the mountains where her people lived. She wondered how long they would be visible. After a walk to the restroom and a stretch, she pulled some munchies from her bag and resumed her reading. John, the main character in the book, had a little boy now, and things were not happy at home. The sun was setting over the Appalachians when Pat finished the book. *What a sad story,* she thought. *At least John made it through all right.*

She pulled a sandwich out of her carry-on bag and ate it quickly. Then she adjusted her pillow, extended her legs as much as was possible in the cramped space allotted to fourth-class passengers, and fell asleep.

Pat woke up to find the sun glaring through the eastern window of the bus. It was morning. She must have been asleep for several hours. Not that it mattered. She had no schedule to keep, and her destination was still a few hours away.

Pat grew nervous as she neared Slidell and the friend who had never known her as a Mennonite. What would Carla think of her now, with her modest dresses and her hair all tucked up in a little covering? Surely, it shouldn't make any difference. Friends are friends, after all.

Pat saw Carla as soon as she stepped off the bus. She looked a little older, but she still had the same baby-blue eyes. "Carla!"

"Pat?" Carla looked puzzled. Then she caught her manners. "It's good to see you. How's life been treating you?"

"My doctor says I'm in good condition for the condition I'm in." They both laughed, glad the awkward moment had passed.

"You took me by surprise, Pat. I don't remember ever seeing you in a dress. Did you make it yourself?" Pat tried not to notice that Carla was staring more at her head-covering than her new dress.

"A friend at church did. She makes all my dresses."

"I didn't know you were a churchgoer."

"Didn't I tell you? I've joined the Mennonites."

"You told me you were associating with them, but I didn't realize you could become one. I thought Mennonites were born that way, like Jews or Russians."

Pat laughed, but not as heartily as usual.

"Yes, well, let's get your luggage."

"So, what sorts of things do you like to do now?" asked Carla as they drove from the bus station to her house.

"Same things I've always done—reading, playing Scrabble, eating out—"

"Movies?"

"Not much."

"Poker?"

"Not really."

"What about shopping?"

"I love to shop." This wasn't turning out at all like Pat had hoped. She hadn't thought her being a Mennonite would have affected their relationship that much, but Carla was clearly uncomfortable with the person Pat had become.

"So," began Carla, when they had settled Pat in the guest room and were sitting on the patio with tall glasses of iced tea. It was still April, and the weather off the Gulf was beautiful. "What made you join the Mennonites?"

"It was a mix of things. I had always believed in God, but I didn't read my Bible or anything. Then, about six or seven years ago, I started to visit my niece in Virginia. She and her husband are Mennonites. They were definitely Christians—anybody could tell that—but they weren't pushy about it. The people at their church were the same way—just so warm and full of love for everybody. I couldn't help but want to join them."

"Did you have to give up electricity and clothes dryers?"

Pat smiled, but not unkindly. "No, that's Amish. Mennonites have microwaves and cars, even computers. My nephew can even take control of people's computers over the phone to fix them. He works for an e-mail company."

"So, what about the dresses? Do you have to wear them all the time?"

"I like my dresses. I just throw them in the washer and dryer, and they come out looking great. I never have to think about what I want to wear."

"Yeah, but what about windy days, or when you want to climb a ladder or something? Surely, you don't wear a dress in the pool!"

"Do I look like I climb ladders or do a lot of swimming?"

"Seriously, Pat, they are so impractical, not to mention old-fashioned. No one wears dresses anymore."

"I do."

Pat and Carla tiptoed around their differences after that, but Pat quickly decided that the week she had anticipated with her old friend was going to be a lot longer than she had imagined. As Sunday approached, her heart began to ache with a longing that was as big as Boyer Hill. As the two women drove to the market on Saturday, Pat noticed a Baptist church on the corner of Carla's street. It was a little white building, not too different-looking from Boyer Hill if you ignored the steeple.

She looked over at Carla, who seemed not to have noticed the church. "We should go there tomorrow. The sign says they have a service at ten; everyone is welcome."

"To church?!"

"Yeah."

"I haven't been to church since I was a kid. I don't think I'd like it any better now that I'm old enough to know better."

"You should try it. The people are probably really nice."

"No thanks."

"Will you drive me then, and pick me up after?"

"I don't mind driving you anywhere, Pat, but don't expect me to go in."

Pat's entire body relaxed the minute she entered the church the next morning. She could almost feel the spirit of worship that pervaded the place, even before the man in the blue suit offered her his hand and a program.

"Welcome to Hill View Baptist. I'm Don. Is this your first time with us?"

"Yes. My first time in Louisiana. I'm Pat Golwitzer."

"Well, you just consider yourself one of the family, Pat. The order of the service is printed right there in your bulletin. If you have any questions, feel free to ask anyone here."

Pat slipped into one of the pews and sat down. People stretched out their hands and introduced themselves as they walked past her. She found their southern accents delightful. How was it that she felt so uneasy with Carla whom she had known for years, yet so comfortable with these people she didn't even know? They were like a breath of spiritual fresh air.

Ahh, the singing! And the prayers. And the sermon. It was like being back at Boyer. Pat's spirits were lifted high, and her soul was refreshed. She could have lingered for hours, but she knew Carla would be waiting for her in the parking lot.

"How was it?" Carla asked when Pat got into the car. "Did people make you feel uncomfortable?"

"Just the opposite. They all came up and shook my hand and wanted to talk with me. They were very friendly."

"You know why, don't you?"

"Because they are nice."

"No, because you look so strange. You were a novelty to them, like something from a book. You know, *novelty? Novel?* Same word."

Pat didn't respond. Carla had just punched the life out of her.

Pat didn't say much the next few days. Neither did Carla. They both knew the visit was over.

chapter 26

Pat was surprised at how relieved she felt to be home. Something fundamental had changed about the way she related to the world and the people in it. "Out there" had become an unpredictable place, a place where friends might not like you anymore, and people could turn and attack without notice.

She unpacked her bags and looked at the calendar on the bedroom wall. Sewing Circle was next Tuesday. It was just what she needed. And it was April, the month to celebrate creativity and new things. In honor of the season, each woman was to prepare some food that took imagination and creativity. *What should I take, stuffed eggs? No, everyone will think of that. Radish roses? Nah, too simple. What about ham? It's not exactly imaginative, but I could decorate it with a creative design of pineapple and maraschino cherries. Yes, I'll make ham.*

Pat had a honey ham tucked away in the back of the fridge. She had bought it last month, thinking they might have it for Easter. Then Joe had bought a different kind of ham, and Becky had made that instead. And they always had pineapple and cherries on hand. Good, that was settled.

"What are you making for Sewing Circle?" Pat asked Becky when she came into the kitchen. "I thought I might slice up the ham that's in there and warm it in the Crock-Pot, if you won't be using it."

"Tuesday is still three days away; I haven't even thought about what to make for supper! But, yeah, go ahead and use the ham. The ladies will love it."

"You could make that salad with mandarin oranges and the sweet dressing."

"Ooh, that's a good idea. I think I have everything for it."

"I'd be happy to make supper," said Pat. "There's a big bag of those chicken tenders from Schwann's. I could make those and some of the vegetables with the bow-tie pasta."

"That would be great, Aunt Pat. Thanks."

"No problem. All it will cost you is a game of Scrabble afterwards."

"Promise?"

"Promise."

"Then it's a deal. You cook, and then I'll whop you at Scrabble."

"Ha!"

Pat slept well that night. She didn't win the Scrabble game—she seldom did. But she was home, and that was all that mattered.

Tuesday came as fast as Tuesdays usually do; too fast if a bill is due, and too slow if you're looking forward to something. Sewing Circle was the highlight of Pat's month, and she had been looking forward to it. She loved sitting and chatting with the ladies from church. Some even drove in from a neighboring church three valleys to the east of Boyer Hill.

The turnout was great. Malinda was there. So were Laura's other three daughters: Vivian, Rosene, and Clara. And, of course, there was Laura's mother Ellen who lived just a bit farther up the ridge. Then there were Valerie, and Rhoda, and Martha, and Vera with her daughter, Jolene. No matter how you counted them, the women filled Wendell and Laura's basement to bursting. Little children filled in the cracks as they ran in and out among the women, sometimes stopping to cut patches, sometimes playing with the toy kitchen set, sometimes going outside to jump on the trampoline. Even Vivian's newborn, Jennifer, showed up for the occasion—though she didn't have much to add to the conversation.

As the other women found places—either standing around the higher table or sitting around the lower one—and began to cut quilt patches from unwanted trousers, Pat sat down to count the patches and group them into bundles. Each finished bundle would be enough to make a full-sized comforter.

Not that the women made the comforters themselves—they just prepared comforter kits to send overseas. By the time they finished with each kit, it would contain enough patches, backing, and thread for some needy woman to make two warm comforters, one for herself and one to give away.

It was an especially good project for the Boyer Hill women because Ellen and Laura and their husbands operated a clothing "rescue mission" in Wendell's shop. Ellen's husband Lester would drive a trailer to town every few weeks to pick up a load of clothes that was no longer wanted by the secondhand shop. Then he and Ellen and all of Wendell's family, would sort the pile of donations. Clothing deemed good enough was packed in shipping bags. The rest was either thrown away or separated by color and stacked in the basement until Sewing Circle day.

The clothing ministry discarded so many unsuitable items that the Sewing Circle could be choosy about what they kept. For the most part, they saved only women's trousers, which stacked neatly and produced several uniform patches per garment.

The women chatted about a variety of things, sometimes in small groups, sometimes all together. After about an hour of such fellowship, Vivian said, "Tell us how your trip was, Aunt Pat." Vivian attended a neighboring church, so she hadn't heard Aunt Pat's report on Sunday.

"It was lousy. I mean the trip itself was great, and the scenery was absolutely gorgeous, but things didn't go too well at my friend's house."

"Why not?"

"Her friend told her she looked funny in her cape dress," chimed in Ellen.

"No!"

"That's exactly how it was. I could tell she didn't like the way I looked from the moment I stepped off the bus. She acted as if I was some kind of major embarrassment or something. Then when I told her how nice everyone at the Baptist church was, she said they were only nice to me because I was weird."

"Well, that's too bad," said Vivian.

"Well, don't you worry about it, Aunt Pat. We think you look just fine," said Ellen. Pat could tell she really meant it.

Smells from Crock-Pots plugged in along the wall started to fill the room. "Mmm, smells like ham," said Laura.

Ellen smiled. "I expect Aunt Pat brought it."

"I'm not telling," said Pat, twinkling. Everyone knew she loved to bring the meat. They were careful to bring something else and leave that to her. "You should see what Clara brought, little cake squares decorated like Scrabble letters. I wonder if she plans on passing them around for dessert or mixing them up in a bag so we can play a round after lunch."

Clara blushed.

"Oh, my!" said Laura. "It's time for devotions. Papa and Wendell will be in any minute." The ladies quickly finished cutting the garment before them and cleared the table. Then they set their chairs in a circle and gave their attention to Malinda. It was her turn to lead devotions.

Malinda began, "I found this little poem about loving other people. I thought it had a good message. It goes like this:

OTHERS

Lord, help me live from day to day
In such a self-forgetful way,
That even when I kneel to pray
My prayer may be for OTHERS.

Help me in all the work I do
To ever be sincere and true,
And know that all I do for you
Must needs be done for OTHERS.

OTHERS, Lord, yes, OTHERS—
And none of self for me;
Help me to live for OTHERS
That I may live for THEE.

Malinda continued, "Jesus said we are to love our neighbors as ourselves. He also said that we should love God with our whole heart and soul and mind and strength. This poem talks about how the two kinds of love are connected. We can't love God without also loving our neighbors."

"Do you suppose that loving God will cause us to automatically love our neighbors?" asked Vivian.

Laura answered, "The Bible says a person who doesn't love his brother whom he has seen can't love the God that he can't see."

"And James says, 'Faith without works is dead,'" added Ellen.

190

"That's right," said Laura. "If we truly love God, we will naturally love others. And if we love others, that shows our love for God."

"I don't suppose you can really separate the two," said Vivian.

Pat thought about what the other women were saying. *You can't love God without loving other people, and you can't love other people without also loving God.* She had never thought about it like that before, but it made sense somehow. The two kinds of love were connected in a way she could feel, but not explain. One thing was for sure, these women had loved her and, in turn, had shown her what God was like.

chapter 27

About a year after Pat moved in with Joe's family, Becky started to get grouchy—well, maybe not so much grouchy, as moody and unpredictable. She began fussing about little things—who sat where, and whether or not Pat put butter on the vegetables. And she made the most outrageous meals, all of which seemed to be based on barley and beans. It seemed that Pat could do nothing right anymore.

"What's with the garbage can in the living room?" Becky asked Pat, who was sitting in the recliner working on an afghan.

"It's so I don't have to get up every time I want to throw away a few threads."

"I'd rather you didn't put it there."

"I can put it over here, if you like," Pat said as she reached down, lifted the small basket, and moved it to the far side of the recliner where it was barely visible to the rest of the room.

"I'd rather not have garbage in the living room at all."

And that was it. Becky said it. Pat was expected to submit without protest. It was maddening!

It was a little easier when Pat learned that Becky had developed some mysterious muscle disease that made her weak and tired all the time. She couldn't even drive the car, so Joe did all the shopping now. Pat missed her drives to town and stopping by the pretty place to listen to the waterfall. She also missed the warm and friendly conversations she and Becky had enjoyed so easily. It was like something precious was ebbing away.

Pat was grateful for the times Malinda took her along when she ran errands. They almost always went out to eat at some nice restaurant that served real food. It was a refreshing break from the twigs and berries Becky usually made.

One Sunday evening, Pat got a phone call that set her heart on edge. Joe had taken his family to the evening service at Vivian's church. Pat had stayed home. About the time the family should have been returning home, Joe called.

"Hello, Aunt Pat. It's Joe."

"Hi, hon. What's up?"

"We're at a friend's house. We'll be staying here for the night."

"Don't you have to work tomorrow?"

"Yeah, but that can wait. Becky isn't quite up to coming home tonight."

"What about her medicines?"

"We can take care of that from here. I'll call you in the morning and let you know what our plans are."

"Okay."

Pat hung up the phone. What did he mean by *what their plans are?* Something in Joe's voice reminded Pat of the way Kevin sounded when he had told her she would have to leave.

She went to bed but couldn't sleep. She couldn't even concentrate on the book she was currently reading, and it was a good one. What did Joe mean by *their* plans? Why didn't he say *our* plans? And why couldn't Becky come home? No, Joe had said *wouldn't,* not *couldn't.* She wouldn't come home. Why?

Pat was weary and ill-rested in the morning. The little sleep she had found had not been at all refreshing. She got up anyway; there was no sense lying in bed wishing for the impossible. She made some rye toast, but it didn't taste good so she tossed it in the garbage. It probably would have upset her stomach anyway.

She got dressed and put up her hair. She may as well be ready for the day, whatever it was going to bring. Sometime around mid-morning, Pastor James and his wife Brenda pulled into the driveway. Pat was glad she had gotten dressed.

"Hi, Aunt Pat," said James, as he came up to the door and shook her hand. "May we come in?"

"Sure."

The three of them sat down in the living room. James began. "I suppose you know why we're here."

"I have an idea."

James continued, "I guess Becky is having a rough time of it."

"So Joe told me."

"It seems she's feeling a lot of stress from trying to blend two families."

"In other words, she wants me to move out."

"Try not to think of it that way. It's probably time you all had your own space."

It was happening again. After a life full of rejection and betrayal, Pat was being thrown out again. She started to cry. Brenda moved over and put her arm around her.

"Where will I go? I can't afford a place of my own."

"Don't be worrying about that. Brenda and I have come to help you look for a place. As a matter of fact, I talked to Jacob on my way here. He and Malinda are calling around to see if they can find something for rent. In the meantime Joe will be taking Becky on a little vacation, so I don't think you need to leave right away."

"I knew this would happen. She promised she'd never kick me out. It was the only reason I agreed to come in the first place."

"Aww, Aunt Pat," said Brenda. "Becky's not rejecting you. She needs a little more space; that's all."

"If this isn't rejection, I don't know what is!"

"Have you eaten?" asked James. "I haven't eaten since six o'clock this morning. What say we go get a bite to eat, and then we'll swing on over to Jacob's to see what he's found out?"

"I'm not very hungry."

"Come on, Aunt Pat," said James. "You've got to keep up your strength. Let's all go to Boyer Station. It'll cheer you up."

"Come on," said Brenda, giving Pat's arm a gentle tug. "I'll help you get your coat."

Boyer Station was a cute little restaurant about a mile south of the church. Pat gained a bit of an appetite when she read over the menu: roast beef, lasagna, fried chicken.

James smiled at her. "Get anything you want; I'm buying."

"The fried chicken looks good."

"Fried chicken it is."

Being with James and Brenda dulled the pain of what Pat was going through. Their compassion and sunny attitude helped Pat to look beyond the circumstances—for a little while, at least. They ate their lunch as leisurely as if the day were absolutely normal. Then the three of them drove over to Jacob and Malinda's house, a mere five minutes from the restaurant.

James dropped Pat at Jacob's house. "Keep your chin up, Aunt Pat. Things are going to work out for the best. Just give it some time."

"If you say so."

She turned to greet Jacob who had stepped out onto his porch.

"Come on in, Aunt Pat," said Jacob. "I think I might have found just the thing for you. A friend of mine has a small trailer in that little trailer park behind Trent's store. She tells me it's fully furnished. It even has dishes, pots and pans, that sort of thing. The only thing it needs is a new set of stairs and an air conditioner. She promised to put in the air conditioner, and I can build the steps for you. Shall we go have a look at it?"

"Sure."

"We'll have to stop at the landlady's house to get the key. It will be a good chance for you to meet one another and talk about arrangements."

In the end, Pat, Jacob, and the landlady all went to the trailer together. Pat had to admit the place really was cute. And with Trent's store right there, it was well-placed.

Pat was lonely in her new home—terribly lonely. There was no one to talk to and not much to do. A sweet lady lived in the trailer across from hers, and the grounds-keeper checked in on her regularly, but it wasn't the same as having people living in the house with her. She was sure she would never adjust to the long and quiet hours between one night and the next. Pat might have gone crazy had not Malinda taken it upon herself to look out for her.

"Knock-knock!" Pat didn't have to say, "Come in." Malinda walked in, even as she announced herself at the door.

"Hi, Aunt Pat!" said Jennalee, Jacob and Malinda's three-year-old. "We brought you some tomatoes."

"Did you grow them yourself?"

"Grandmother did, but we had too many so Mama thought you would want them."

"I was just thinking about a fat, juicy tomato sandwich on toast. You want to share one with me?"

"Actually," interjected Malinda, "I have to run to town to get some parts for Jacob. I thought you might like to ride along."

"If you twist my arm. Let me get my purse."

Malinda was a friend to Pat in other ways too. She changed her light bulbs, unclogged the kitchen drain, and drove her to doctor's appointments. Most of all, Malinda listened. No matter how often or how long Pat talked about her loneliness, her fears, or her dreams, Malinda always listened.

Other people from church stepped in too. Valerie brought her the sale items from the grocery store in town; Jolene popped in for visits with her daughter, Kristalyn; and Laura picked her up and brought her to the clothing center so Pat could spend an afternoon sorting clothes.

Eventually, as she recovered much of her strength, even Becky began to come around more—driving Pat to doctor's appointments and having her over on Sunday afternoons for dinner and a game or two of Scrabble. And though it was nice to have her niece in her life again, it was not quite the same as being a regular part of the family.

á·dop′tion, *the*
adopt.] *the*
being adopted;
treating of the child of another
(b) the taking into fellowship

chapter 28

Pat adjusted to living on her own, but without her own car, she felt like a burden. Jacob or Vera's husband David readily offered to drive her to church, and several of the ladies took her with them when they went shopping. But they weren't family, and she always felt like she was being a bother.

On the other hand, Pat grew closer to people she hadn't gotten to know when she had gone everywhere with Becky. Like David. He sat way over on the men's side at church, and he tended to be rather quiet even when he was mixing with the larger group. But in the car he talked about all kinds of things—gardens, community news, the Bible— and his words were always sweet or inspiring.

And there was Jennifer. She was single, like Pat, so they had many things in common.

Eventually a regular schedule was worked out for who would drive Pat to church. Jacob and Malinda would come unless they were sick or out of town, at which time David and Vera would pick her up. Both couples drove right past her trailer park on their way to church, so Pat didn't feel like picking her up was a burden. However, a system like this is only as good as the communication of its members, and the day came when someone forgot to tell someone else that the other party was supposed to pick up you-know-who.

November 2, 2008, was an unusually warm and pleasant day for the Highlands. Pat sat looking out the large glass door facing the entrance to the trailer park. It was where she sat every Sunday morning, because it gave her a direct view of everyone who drove up to her home.

This morning she was waiting for Jacob and Malinda. It was already 9:50; Sunday school would begin in ten minutes, and it took them a good five minutes to drive from her place to church. Where were they?

When Jacobs still hadn't arrived by 9:55, Pat grabbed her sweater and walked out the front door. She and Jacob had agreed that if ever they were late she was to go sit out on the bench beside the newspaper box at Trent's Store right on the main road. Picking her up there might give them the few extra seconds they would need to avoid being late. She hadn't had to wait at Trent's very often, but it was not totally foreign to her.

Trent's was a deep building, the back of which stretched right past the end of Pat's trailer, so she didn't have far to the bench: down the steps, across the small lawn, and around to the front of the building.

She sat facing the gas pump and the road beyond and settled in to wait. A yellow-and-white Mini Cooper pulled up to the pump. That was an odd sight, such a sporty vehicle in this off-the-map town. Even more odd was the man who stepped out of the snazzy car. He was an older gentleman in casual clothes and a full beard that couldn't hide his smile. It wasn't that he was odd-looking on his own; Pat just had trouble matching him with the car he drove.

"Mornin', ma'am," he said as he walked up to the newspaper box beside her bench. "A fine day we're having."

"You're not kidding. Who would have thought it was November?"

It was typical small-town talk—friendly, nonthreatening, but of little content other than to make a *hello* last longer.

The man dropped a few coins into the newspaper box and pulled out the Sunday paper, leaving Pat to her thoughts. What a life she had lived! From the crime and filth-ridden projects of a dying city, to a rough-hewn bench outside a rustic country store. It had been a good life, despite all the uphill climbs, and Pat was happy to have been given the chance to live it.

Where were Jacob and Malinda? Pat looked at her watch. It was past ten already. What could be keeping them?

"Mr. Mini Cooper" tucked the newspaper under his arm and looked down at Pat. "You waiting for someone?"

"Well, I was waiting for my ride to church, but I guess they're not coming."

"You from that Mennonite church up on the hill?" There was another advantage to wearing a cape dress and covering.

"Yeah."

"Hop in. I'm heading right past there."

Pat got up and walked the few steps to the car without a cautious thought or suspicion crossing her mind. She got into the passenger seat and closed the door. Mr. Cooper got in beside her and started the car.

"Aren't you the folks that mail those *Reaching Out* magazines every so often?"

"Yeah."

"I just love that magazine. I read every page. It's a real good thing you're doing there."

"Thanks." Pat had helped to fold the last batch of outreach magazines just a few weeks before, after a Wednesday night service. She wondered if he had gotten one of hers in the mail.

The Mini Cooper pulled up to the front of the church where, through the open door, the pastor's son Richard, could be seen leading the congregation in singing. His jaw dropped and his hand stopped beating the time when he saw Pat emerge from the sports car. She thoroughly enjoyed the moment and leaned into the car to thank the driver one more time.

"You're mighty welcome, ma'am. Have a great day."

"You too."

Richard had regained his composure by the time Pat entered the foyer, but both Larry, who could see her from his position on the platform, and Karen, who had turned around to see what had amazed Richard, stared at Pat as she walked in. Karen motioned for her to come near.

"What?" asked Pat as quietly as she could. She knew she was already disturbing the service by walking in late.

"Where are Laura and Vera?" Karen asked.

"Laura and Vera? How should I know?"

"Didn't you see them at your place?"

"No. I wasn't at my place. I was waiting for Jacob at Trent's."

Pat sat down and tried extra hard to get into the spirit of worship. She was glad when she saw Karen slip out the door and get into her car; she must be going to check on Jacob's. About the time Pat had put off the strangeness of the morning and was beginning to concentrate on Larry's sermon, Karen returned. *Ah, good,* thought Pat. *Jacob's must be okay.* A while later, Vera and Laura walked in. Laura's dress was wrinkled and wisps of Vera's hair uncharacteristically escaped from beneath her covering. They both relaxed visibly when they saw Pat. Then they slid silently into the back pew. *What in the world?*

Pat, Laura, Vera, and Karen rushed up to one another as soon as the service ended. Larry and Richard craned their necks from afar.

Laura started. "Aunt Pat, what happened to you this morning?"

"I was going to ask you the same question," said Pat, confused.

"When you didn't come in with David's this morning, I thought maybe Jacob's were going to bring you. So I called their place, and there was no answer. I figured you were all on your way, so I sat down for the service. When you still weren't here after the second song, I whispered to Karen to find out if Jacob's were supposed to be coming. She said no, they were on a trip. So I got up and made another call to your house. But you didn't answer. That's when I really worried."

"I was at Trent's."

"What for?"

"That's where I wait when Jacob is late."

Understanding dawned on Laura's face. She laughed. "Oh, dear!"

"What?"

"We just broke into your house for nothing."

"You what?!"

"Ha! When I couldn't get hold of you, I told Becky and Vera and Karen about it. They said somebody should go make sure you were all right. So Vera and I went, and Becky and Karen stayed here in case you came in while we were gone. We never thought to look at Trent's.

"We knocked on your door, then on the windows. We really worried when you didn't answer, so Vera went over and asked your neighbor if she had seen you. She said she hadn't.

"We figured we'd better find a way in to check on you. Vera suggested seeing if we could push the window up over the air conditioner. I got a lawn chair for her to stand on. When she pushed up the window, the air conditioner began to fall out! We caught it and moved the chair over and set the air conditioner on it.

"Then I went tearing around the front of the trailer to get a trash can for Vera to stand on, but I slipped on the hardtop and fell." Laura extended her leg to show the scuff marks on her shoe. A cut was visible on her finger.

"That's quite the adventure," said Pat.

"Oh, that's not all," replied Laura.

"We got the trash can in place, and Vera climbed on it and in through the window. She unlocked the door so I could get in. We searched all the rooms, dreading that we would find you unconscious, or worse.

"Then Karen pulled in and said, 'The Lord works in mysterious ways; Aunt Pat is at church!' So Karen went back to church while Vera and I put everything back together. I'm afraid we might have damaged your window, Aunt Pat."

"As long as you didn't break my air conditioner!"

Richard walked up. "Nice car, Aunt Pat!"

"Oh, yeah, I just got it."

"Who was the driver?"

"Just some nice man who was buying a paper at Trent's."

Becky chimed in. "You mean you got into a car with a man you don't even know?!"

"I needed a ride to church."

chapter 29

at stared at the bags of coffee resting beside the rolls of wrapping paper and ribbon on the table before her, and wondered what would be the best way to wrap them. Malinda was her secret sister that year and loved good coffee, so Pat had gotten her a few bags the last time she had passed through a Tim Horton's. While she was deliberating between a matching red ribbon and a shiny white bow, the phone rang. It was Harry.

"Hi, Ma." *Was that a catch in his voice?*

"Hi, hon. Is something wrong?"

"Kind of. I lost my job. Then I couldn't pay the mortgage. I lost the house too. I got nowhere to go and no money."

"You can come stay with me. I've got an extra bedroom."

"Oh, Ma, I'd love to. But you'd have to come get me. I don't have a car or nothing."

"Don't worry about that. I'll work out something from here. You just sit tight, and I'll come get you, okay?"

"Okay."

"You'll be okay 'til I get there?"

"Yeah."

Pat called Becky and a few others from church, but before she even had a chance to call everyone, Valerie called her instead.

"Pat, what's this I hear about your boy needing a ride to get down here?"

"Oh, Valerie, he's lost his house, his job, everything. And he says he'd like to come stay with me, but I have no way to get him."

"Oh, yes, you do! I'll drive you. We can leave as soon as you're ready."

Pat started to cry. Somehow she had held it in until then, but Valerie's willingness to drop everything and drive a thousand miles to pick up someone else's son was more than Pat's emotions could contain.

"Oh, Valerie, I don't know what to say."

"Then don't say anything. Just pack your bags and we'll get going."

Pat called her sister Mary to arrange a place for them to stay. The trip was going to take eight hours each way. They would need a place to rest before they headed back home. Then she packed her bag.

As she sat in the chair waiting for Valerie, Pat looked at the large hanging on the wall over the couch. It was a woven picture of a horse in a meadow at the edge of a peaceful mountain stream. Across the picture in black script were the words to Psalm 23. She had lost her little Psalm 23 plaque somewhere in the move to West Virginia.

So, when she had seen the woven hanging advertised in a magazine, she had ordered one as a replacement.

God had been such a good Shepherd for her all these years, guiding and guarding her even before she knew who He really was. Now she was going to have Harry with her again. She prayed she could be the kind of mother he needed.

Valerie and Pat had been driving for several hours, talking on and off about a variety of subjects, when Pat confessed that she had not eaten at all that day.

"You haven't eaten anything?!" said Valerie.

"Well, Harry called before I had a chance to get breakfast, and I was too upset to eat after that."

"Then we're just going to pull in at the next restaurant we see."

Pat squirmed a bit, knowing how little money was in her purse. "Let's just stop at a gas station and get a roller dog or something."

Valerie looked at Pat. "Are you low on cash, Aunt Pat?"

"Well, I wasn't planning on a trip right now."

"You just relax. This trip is on me. We're going to sit down to a nice, hot dinner, and you're not going to worry about what it costs. The Lord has already provided for all that."

"But you have your own family. It's enough that you are taking time from them; I can't ask you to pay for it as well."

"You didn't ask. I offered. Consider it a gift from the Lord and thank Him for the way He always takes care of us." The twenty-third psalm echoed in Pat's mind again:

Thou preparest a table before me . . . my cup runneth over. It was all so true!

Pat and Valerie arrived at Dave and Mary's house after dark. It was too late to get Harry that day, so they settled in for the evening with Pat's sister and brother-in-law.

"So Harry's moving to the hills," Mary said, but it was more like a question than a statement.

Pat answered, "He's got nothing, Mary. When they closed the plant there was nowhere for him to go. No work, no pay, no mortgage money. That house was his pride and joy. It must have torn him apart to have to give it up."

"He always did keep it in good shape. What did they do, auction it?"

"All I know is they cleared out all his stuff when he was gone one day and put new locks on the doors. They didn't even leave him his wallet. They cleared out everything."

"Surely they put it in storage somewhere."

"If they did, they're not telling him where."

"You mean he has no ID?"

"He's got nothing, Mary, absolutely nothing."

"Can he get replacements for his identification?" asked Valerie.

"He may sometime in the future. All he wants right now is to get away and forget about it all."

"I can't blame him," said Mary. "That's a lot for one man to lose. So he's going to live with you?"

"Yeah, I have two bedrooms. The one has the freezer and a bunch of shelves, but we'll make room. He can sleep on the couch if he has to."

"You plan on driving back to West Virginia in the morning?"

"As soon as we pick up Harry."

"Then you ought to be getting some sleep. The couch opens up to a bed, or you can sleep on the recliners, if you like. The blankets are over there," Mary pointed to a pile of bedding beside the couch.

"Thanks a million, Mary."

"No problem."

Pat and Valerie picked up Harry early the next morning and began their homeward journey. Harry didn't say much during the drive, and they didn't pressure him. It was enough to know he was safe, and wanted, and on his way to a new future.

chapter 30

Harry brought a brightness into Pat's life. It's not that they had long talks, or shared their deepest hopes and dreams, but they were there for each other. Pat provided Harry with a home, and he gave her money when he found odd jobs. They shared mealtimes and household chores and short conversations about the rising cost of gasoline, the best way to grill a steak, and how to keep the squirrels out of the bird feeder.

"Harry! David and Vera are here!" called Pat. She grabbed her Bible bag, a bottle of water, and her Sunday school supplies. Pat was Jennalee's teacher this year, and she liked to be prepared. Harry came into the room.

"Should I grab the Crock-Pot?" he asked.

"Yeah, and that cake dish too, if you can manage it."

"No problem."

It was Sunday, and Boyer Hill was planning a fellowship meal. Pat had made her famous hamburgers in tomato soup and a cake covered with sprinkles. The children always loved the sprinkles.

When the Sunday school superintendent announced that it was time for the preschool class to go to their room, Pat grabbed her bag in one hand, Jennalee's hand in the other, and headed for the stairs.

She was only halfway down the stairs when she slipped. Thankfully, she caught herself or she would have rolled to the bottom. Her knees had grown steadily worse, and it was getting more difficult to manage the stairs in either direction.

Then she thought of Oscar, the dear old man who sat in the back of the men's section. His knees were much worse than hers—which wasn't surprising, given that he was in his nineties. He was such a cheerful person, smiling through the entire sermon as if he heard every word James said—though everyone knew he was stone deaf. Oscar couldn't manage the stairs at all. So whenever he was at church, the women held their class downstairs so that Oscar could meet with the men in the main auditorium.

Pat loved her class as much as Jennalee did. Together they read Bible stories, colored pictures, and sang short songs. Given her relatively recent entry into the church, it was a good assignment for Pat, who learned almost as much from their lessons as Jennalee did.

After Sunday school and the church service, everyone drove to the picnic area at Old House Run in the National Forest for a fellowship meal. Old House was one of Boyer Hill's favorite places to spend a lazy Sunday afternoon— beautiful, shady, and right beside a softly-flowing stream.

People made their way to the small pavilion and spread their food upon the table in the customary order: hot foods first, then salads, and finally, desserts.

"Do I smell meatballs?" asked Malinda, setting a bowl of broccoli salad in the middle of the table.

"Hamburgers in tomato soup."

"It smells wonderful, whatever it is."

Jolene's husband Clement set a bowl of suspicious-looking meat on the table.

Pat looked at it and sniffed. "What have you got there, 'possum?"

Clement scratched his head and looked down at his shirt. "Oh, I don't know, just something Jolene fixed." He had been known to offer groundhog, guinea, and who knew what else, to unsuspecting diners—all with a hint of silent satisfaction. The thing was, it all tasted so good, and you didn't know what you were eating until the meal was over, when he confessed. This time it looked like bear in gravy. Pat liked the way Jolene fixed bear. She would have to be sure to get some.

Pastor James led in prayer, and everyone filled their plates with food. Becky sat on the bench beside Pat.

"Have you heard anything from your mom lately?" asked Pat.

"I talked to her yesterday. It seems they've got a new priest at St. Michael's—a Father Jack, something or other. Marshall—that's it, Jack Marshall."

"The name sounds familiar. Did he ever preach while I was at St. Michaels?"

"Not that I remember. Though, you're right. Something about the name strikes a bell."

"What does she think of him?"

"She likes him. She says he's easy to understand. But he's only there part-time. The congregation is too small to pay him full-time, and he has a family; so he works somewhere else during the week—a hospice, I think she said."

"Are you having scrapbooking at your house this Saturday?" asked Pat between bites. Gathering with a few of the ladies to work on their scrapbook pages was one of Pat's favorite outings.

"I'm planning on it."

"We seem to be meeting less and less lately."

"Everyone's just so busy."

"Look out!" yelled Harry as the football slammed onto the table and bounced onto the ground behind Pat. "Sorry about that. You know how these footballs are."

"They seem to be especially independent-minded right after they leave your hands," said Becky.

Harry grinned at her. "It must be the high altitude."

"Must be." She grinned back at him. So did Pat. It was good to see how well Harry had adjusted over the past two years. He acted as if he had been born in the hills. It did Pat's heart good to watch him.

She was just as blessed to watch him get ready for work the next morning. He had contracted to remodel a house right around the corner from the trailer park. He sang snatches of old songs as he puttered around the kitchen throwing together a boxed lunch. "You got any plans today Ma?" he asked.

"Not much. I might go over to the senior center with Karen."

"Sounds like fun. Be good!" With that, he went out the door, and Pat was left alone. She sighed, resigned herself to the loneliness, and settled back in her recliner to read the next book in the never-ending pile of novels that kept her from going crazy. She used to lead a very active life; now she only read about them.

She had just found her place when the phone rang.

"Hello, Pat. Are you sitting down?" It sounded like her sister Mary.

"Yeah. Why?" Mary was not the melodramatic sort. What could be wrong?

"Would you like to talk to your daughter?"

"What are you talking about? Who is this?" She had thought it was Mary, but the conversation made no sense.

"It's Mary. Would you like to talk to your daughter—the baby—you know, Suzzane."

"Mary, you're making no sense. What are you talking about?"

"Suzzane—I have her phone number."

chapter 31

"How?" asked Pat, caught so off guard that her brain could think in only the shortest of sentences. "You mean my Suzzane? You have her phone number? How did you get it?"

"She's the pastor's wife—at St. Michael's. Except her name isn't Suzzane anymore; it's Mary," answered Pat's sister.

"And she's your pastor's wife?"

"Yes. Father Jack connected our names and figured out that you were his wife's mother. Then he told her about it and called here to see if I had a sister named Patricia who had given up a daughter, and if you wanted to call her."

"Oh. Sure, I want to call her. She knows I'll be calling?"

"Father Jack told her first."

"What's her number?"

Pat grabbed a pen and jotted down the number her sister gave her. Then she took a minute to catch her breath. Suzzane, her Suzzane. After all these years, they had found her Suzzane. *Her name is not Suzzane anymore; it's Mary. Why did they change her name?* Suzzane, Mary, what did it matter? She was her baby in either case. No, she wasn't her baby either; she must be forty-some years old by now. Whee!

Pat dialed the number, slowly at first, then faster, as if she needed to make the connection before she woke up to find it was all just a dream.

"Hello," said a soft, sweet, but hesitant voice.

"Is this Mary?" asked Pat, just as haltingly.

"First, tell me; what's my birth date?" said the voice, now stronger, but still guarded.

"August eighth, nineteen sixty-six."

"Okay. And you are?"

"Patricia Golwitzer."

"Was that your birth name?"

"No, my maiden name was Vohwinkel."

"Did you give a child up for adoption?"

"I gave up my daughter Suzzane Vohwinkel. It was the hardest thing I've ever done."

"Oh my."

Both women were silent for a while. There was no way either of them could talk through their tears.

Mary spoke first. "I am your daughter, then."

"I can hardly believe it! I have searched for you ever since I first gave you up. They told me the adoptive parents had kept your name, so I was searching for Suzzane. But you are Mary now. That's a pretty name. My sister is named Mary. Oh, you know that!"

The light humor briefly slowed the flow of tears.

"Yes, I know Mary Noonan. Not very well, but she goes to St. Michael's where Jack is the pastor. That's how I found you—or he found you, rather. He was looking over the parish records trying to learn about the congregation when he came across your sister's maiden name. He had found out a long time ago that my birth name had been Vohwinkel, so when he saw Vohwinkel on your sister's baptismal record, he was amazed. He had never seen the name before, except on my birth record."

"And to think I used to go to St. Michael's."

"You did?!"

"Yeah, but that was years ago—oh, I don't know, maybe a good fifteen to twenty years. Were you there then?"

"No, we've only been here a few months."

"That's incredible. Think of how many churches there are, and we ended up going to the same one."

"I know. Were you at St. Michael's when I was born?"

"No, I didn't attend any church back then. If I had, it would probably have been Catholic. That's why I had you baptized Catholic."

"I was raised Catholic too."

"But St. Michael's is an Episcopal church. How did you end up there?"

"It's a long story. My husband is an Episcopalian priest. How did *you* end up there if you were Catholic?"

"It's a long story too."

Silence again.

Finally Pat spoke. "Did you have a happy childhood? I mean, have things gone well for you?"

"For the most part. I had my ups and downs like anybody, but my parents loved me and gave me a good home. I actually thought about trying to find you sometimes, but I thought it would hurt my mother's feelings, as if I didn't love her or that she wasn't good enough somehow. She was a great mom."

"You say *was*. Is she gone?"

"She died a few years ago."

Pat choked up. "It's all I wanted for you, that you would be happy. It's the only reason I gave you up, you know."

Silence. This was getting too deep too fast. Neither Pat nor Mary was prepared to deal with all of what it meant to find one another after a lifetime apart.

"This is a lot to process all at once," said Mary through her sobs. "I'm really glad we've found each other, but I need time to think—and to blow my nose." They both laughed, grateful for the relief. "Why don't we say good-bye for now, and I can call you again in a few days, after we've had some time to think?"

"I think that's a good idea."

Mother and daughter said good-bye. Both of them knew that this time it would not be forever.

Pat sat in her chair and cried for a long, long time. After all the years of wondering and searching and longing, when thoughts of ever having a daughter had receded to the mistier corners of her mind, she was able to contact the one person she had longed for most in this world. Her heart swelled and felt as if it would burst from the ecstasy of it all. Hers was the heart that had been abused by her father, abandoned by her men, and rejected by one person after another. She didn't know what to do with this new emotion, this reaching out from the only person she had, herself, abandoned.

She didn't deserve Suzzane's love. Ma had convinced her of that—Pat was a bad mother who had let someone else raise her daughter. Ma didn't understand though. Pat had loved Suzzane, loved her with a love so deep she was able to give her away rather than see her suffer. And Suzzane still wanted her. Had she forgiven her? Did she hold any bitterness in her heart toward the mother who had given her away? Surely she must. But then she couldn't possibly understand how it was. Pat would have to tell her how hard it was, how awful her life would have been if she had stayed with her and Harry.

Pat spent the next few days in a fog, her mind drifting from the past to the present, to the future that might be. It was then that worry broke through. What would everyone at church think when they found out she had given up her own baby? She would have to tell them. It would come out one way or another anyway.

Then again, maybe Mary would never call back. Maybe that one phone conversation was all she would ever have. That would serve her right. She had rejected her daughter, so her daughter would reject her. What could be fairer? Pat was a fool to get her hopes up. Why did she trust people anyway?

Mary did call back. She, too, had needed time to work through the sudden shock of finding her very own blood mother.

After warming up with discussions about the weather, Pat broached a question that had been puzzling her. "You said your husband connected you with me when he saw the name Vohwinkel on my sister's church records. But, how did he know that my name was Vohwinkel at all?"

"Jack was a Catholic priest before we got married, though we were good friends even then. As part of his work one day, he had access to my birth certificate. He noticed a name crossed out and looked closer. On the line where my mother's name was supposed to be, was the name Patricia Vohwinkel. It had been only lightly scratched out, and my mother's name was written above it."

"I thought they completely blacked out the name in sealed birth records," said an astounded Pat.

"They were supposed to. Someone slipped up."

"I'm sure glad they did!"

"Me too."

"So, Jack knew your name had been Vohwinkel even before you were married?"

"Yes. But he knew I didn't want to look for you, because I thought it might hurt my mom. So, he wrote the name down and stuck it in his wallet. He's kept it there—"

"Until he saw it again on my sister's church records."

"Right."

"This is absolutely unbelievable!" said Pat. "To think, he kept that name for all these years."

"Jack couldn't believe it either. When he called your sister Mary, and found out that she had a sister named Patricia, who had given up a daughter for adoption in 1966, he knew you were my mother."

"What did you do when you found out?"

"Honestly, I didn't know what to do. I had pushed aside the idea of contacting you for so long, it took a while to decide what I wanted. But my mom had died, so—"

"So you let me call. I'm so glad you did."

"I am too."

chapter 32

I t was strange telling Harry about Suz—uh, Mary. Oh, he had known that he had a sister and that she had been given up at birth. But to tell him that she had been found . . .

He took it as matter-of-factly as he took anything.

"Great news, Ma. You going to see her?"

"Hopefully over Thanksgiving."

"That'll be sweet."

And that was that. Telling the church would not be as easy.

They were part of her life now, part of her family. No, it was deeper than that even. They were a part of her. She could hardly go around pretending nothing had changed in her life, nor did she want to. She decided to tell them the next Sunday.

Pat woke with bleary eyes and a sick stomach on Sunday. Not that she had slept much. Thoughts of Mary had filled the night hours. Memories of how she had looked that day in the hospital chapel so long ago, and imaginations of what she might look like now, would have been enough to make sleep hard to find, but worries about the rejection she was sure to face when she confessed what she had done, had made falling asleep almost impossible.

She grabbed her purple dress and put it on. It was a cheerful pattern and lightened her spirits a bit when she looked at it. She pinned her hair into a quick bun and clipped on her whitest covering. There, at least she looked good on the outside.

She glanced at the loaf of bread on the counter, then thought better of it. She was holding steady with an empty stomach; there was no telling what would happen if she ate. She grabbed her Bible and Sunday school quarterly and sat down in the recliner to wait for her ride. Pat opened the quarterly to review the day's lesson, but the words made no sense. How could they make sense when all of her energy was being diverted to producing stomach acid and tapping her fingers?

"This is ridiculous!" she said, and got up to go fill the bird feeder. It was down a quarter; she may as well fill it now. That done, she sat on the porch chair to wait. Fortunately, Jacob and Malinda weren't long in coming or she would surely have worn a finger hole in the arm of the chair from the incessant tapping.

Pat pretended to pay attention to the Sunday school lesson, and she looked absolutely absorbed in the sermon. The truth was, she didn't hear a word. She was about to announce to her closest friends what a wretch she was, and she could think of nothing else.

"Does anyone have something they'd like to share?" asked James, after the closing song. It was a customary part of the service, and the opportunity Pat had been dreading for several days. She raised her hand. "Yes, Aunt Pat."

She cleared her throat and began. "In my youth, I was rather naive, and I fell for a man who said he loved me, but he didn't. I gave birth to a baby daughter. I already had Harry, and I had no income, and I knew there was no way I could support her. So I gave her up for adoption with the hopes that she would go to a good family and have the kind of life I could never give her." Tears streamed down her face. She dried them on her sleeve. Ellen, sitting beside her, started to cry. Pat could hear sniffing all around the room.

"Well, I got a call the other day from my sister. It turns out her pastor's wife was also adopted, and she has my name on her birth certificate, even though it was supposed to have been completely erased. We've talked on the phone, and she is definitely my daughter."

James looked down from the pulpit in astonishment. "That's wonderful!" he said. "Are you planning for a reunion any time soon?"

"I'm hoping to get up there in November."

Pat dried her eyes again.

"God sure does work in mysterious ways," said James, as he dried his own eyes.

After a short prayer and a final verse of song, everyone gathered around Pat to give her tearful hugs and other well-wishes.

"You hear about stuff like this in storybooks," said Ellen, with the warmest smile, "but you never expect it to be sitting right beside you in church!"

"I can hardly believe it myself!"

"You say you're hoping to meet her in November?" asked Laura.

"Well, the whole family is planning to get together for Thanksgiving. I was already planning to ride up with Becky. So, I'll just spend Thanksgiving Day with them, and then meet Mary the day after."

"Mary. Is that your daughter's name?" asked Ellen.

"Well, I named her Suzzane, but her parents changed it to Mary when they got her. It feels kind of weird to call her Mary when I've thought of her as Suzzane all these years."

"How old is she?" asked Ellen.

"Forty-four."

"She's not a baby anymore!"

"No, and I have no idea what she looks like. I try to imagine Harry with long hair, but I think she's much prettier than that."

"Let's hope so!"

Everyone laughed. Then they smiled and continued to ask as many questions as Pat could answer. Not one of them held even a hint of condemnation.

Pat felt as light and carefree when she got home as she had felt weighed down and anxious that morning. Rather than scorning or condemning her when they found out about Mary, everyone had rejoiced with her. What incredible people she had been blessed with at Boyer Hill! They just loved and loved and kept on loving. Pat felt more blessed than she knew a person could be.

She turned her thoughts toward the trip in November and all the things she might like to share with Mary when they met. She would probably love to learn all about her brothers, and her grandparents and aunts and uncles. And she'd want to know about Pat's illustrious career as a top-notch secretary. She'd probably like to see pictures too.

Pat's sons—front: Peter; back: Harry, Brian, and Eddie.

That gave Pat a great idea; she would gather some pictures into a nice photo book that she could give to Mary. That way she could refer to it whenever she was curious about her relatives.

Pat set about sorting through her old photos. It was a pleasant task, as she relived some good memories while she sorted through the pictures. There was a great shot of her with Kevin and Ma, but that one probably wouldn't interest Mary; Kevin wouldn't mean much to her. Ah, there was one of Ma by herself; that was a good one. Pat put it aside. Mary would like that one. She picked up the one with all four of her sons on a rock together. What a handsome bunch of boys they were!

The pictures of Dad were not as painful to look at as they once had been. He really had grown milder with age, and Pat had softened too. It's funny how we understand the sins of others better when we have failed too.

Too bad there weren't any pictures of Vince. Pat never thought she would feel that way, but it would have been nice to be able to show Mary what her father looked like. He was handsome, after all, and he did have a lot of winsome qualities. Pat hadn't heard any news about Vince in years. She didn't even know if he was still alive. Oh well, she guessed Mary could look him up if she wanted to. For herself, he was a part of her life best left in the past.

She picked up a picture of herself as a baby. Look at that ear! It was the dreaded Vohwinkel ear. Pat had been unfortunate enough to inherit it. Why, from the angle in the picture, the appendage looked full half the size of the rest of her head. No need to send that picture. She didn't want to scare Mary off every time she looked at it.

Eventually, Pat narrowed her selections to the few best pictures and put them in a little book, in chronological order. She flipped through it with satisfaction; her heart warmed that she could at least give Mary this much of her history.

à·dop'tion, adopt.] the being adopted; treating of the child of ano... (b) the taking into fellows... s. the ado...

chapter 33

I t was the fourth Monday in November—only three days until Thanksgiving. The day after Thanksgiving, Pat would meet Mary. She stared into her closet, wondering which dresses to pack. Memories of Carla's reaction haunted her as she looked at the choices. Purple? Green? Floral? All of her dresses were cape dresses of course. Had Mary ever seen a cape dress? Had she ever seen a Mennonite? How would she feel about her own mother being one? It was one thing to talk on the phone, where voices alone gave clues about a person, but to be seen in person brought a whole new level of knowing, and of risk.

Pat was no longer the pretty young woman who had held a tiny baby, forty-four years ago. She was at the far end of middle-aged—old-aged if you judged by her medications—with a few gray hairs and more weight than she cared to show off.

Then again, Mary was no baby anymore either. She was a woman in her own right, and probably as nervous as Pat.

Pat carefully folded her four best dresses and tucked them into the suitcase beside her other items. Then she picked up the photo book she had made for Mary, wrapped it in a towel, and nestled it gently on top. It had seemed like such a wonderful gift when she had made it. Now it seemed tiny and insignificant. Photos could not replace the life that had been denied Mary. What was a picture compared to a mother's love?

But Mary had known a mother's love, and a father's besides. That was more than she could have gotten from Pat alone. Oh, it was all so confusing! Pat shut the suitcase and determined not to look into it again until she was at her sister's house.

"Are you excited about Friday?" asked Becky, across the Scrabble board. It was Tuesday evening, and Pat had come to spend the night at Joe and Becky's so they could pull out early in the morning.

"Yeah. It's kind of nerve-wracking, though."

"It's got to be weird, thinking about meeting your own child, when you haven't seen one another since practically the day she was born."

"Tell me about it!"

Pat slept surprisingly well that night. Perhaps it was the fact that she had fretted through so many sleepless nights the past week that she couldn't stay awake any longer. In any case, she was glad for the rest.

The eight-hour drive went much faster than usual. Everything was speeding up, it seemed. Pat didn't talk much, though. It was enough to be surrounded by conversation

238

and the company of people she loved being with. Besides, they provided a distraction from her nervous anticipation.

Her sister's house was packed with company; so many people, in fact, that Joe had rented a couple of motel rooms for his group. Still, they were at the house all day, and the place was gloriously packed. Pat counted twenty-six people one time, and she was sure she must have missed someone.

The house was too small to hold that many people for a big meal, though, so they moved the party to the home of her nephew Craig for the actual Thanksgiving celebration. The meal served that year was almost beyond description. Suffice it to say that there were enough ancillary vegetables and varieties of pie to do justice to the three turkeys and four different kinds of sweet potato casseroles set out on the board!

"Mary, you brought your apple crumb pie! You know it's my favorite."

"Yeah, well, it's my favorite too," teased Dave, as he scooped up the apple pie and threatened to make off with it. "This one's all mine."

"Not unless you can tackle me for it," said Craig in turn, as he sneaked up behind his father and grabbed the pie right out of his unsuspecting hands. To Pat's great relief, he placed it gently back on the table where everyone would have a fair shot at it. Not that anyone needed to worry. There were three identical pies waiting right beside it!

One would have thought the amount of food eaten on Thursday would have kept everyone in good form until at least Saturday afternoon, but, by Friday, they were at it again. Dave had arranged to have the group meet in the basement of St. Michael's this time, partly because they could spread out so well, and partly because it seemed like a natural place for Pat and Mary to have their first meeting.

Pat's hands trembled as she rode in the backseat. Dave was taking her to the church early, so she and Mary could have some time to get to know one another before the rest of the family arrived. Now that it came to it, Pat wasn't sure she could go through with it. Mary had every reason to resent her, to hold her responsible for all the wrongs ever done to her. And, there was the matter of the dress—and the covering. Pat liked her plain clothing—and she didn't usually mind looking out of fashion—but this time was different. This was her child, and she wanted to be liked, looked up to—at least respected.

Fortunately, it wasn't far to St. Michael's. Before Pat had time to work herself up into a full-blown anxiety attack, Dave was pulling up to the church. Memories washed over Pat as she looked at the homey, brick building with its white trim and stained-glass windows. Memories of that first Sunday morning, when Bob and Carol had greeted her at the door; and of God assuring her that Peter would be healed; and of the anger she felt at the people who had made her sister cry at Ma's memorial service. The memories brought with them a flood of emotions that swirled and coalesced and found a spot beside the nervousness she felt about meeting Mary.

Dave held the door for her as she walked into the building. Soon, she would see her daughter. Her heart pounded as she made her way to the basement and turned the corner that led to the fellowship hall where waited . . . Mary!

"Oh, Mary!" Pat ran as she hadn't for years, across the room to where Mary waited with outstretched arms. "Mary." Mother and daughter held one another as if they were afraid of being parted again. It would have been hard to tell who cried which tears, as drops of pent-up longings fell from their eyes and mingled on their clothing. Neither woman noticed at all what the other was wearing.

Finally satisfied that Mary was truly real, Pat noticed the man and two children standing nearby. "This is my husband Jack," said Mary, in a voice that reminded Pat of dollhouses and swing sets and laughing brooks, all at the same time. "And these are our children. Kyle is fourteen, and Elena just turned eleven. Justin and Nicole couldn't make it."

"Hi, guys," said Pat. It was strange enough to see Mary, whom she had dreamed about for years—but new grandchildren! It was overwhelming. Apparently it was just as overwhelming to the children, who seemed hard-pressed to know how one is to act toward a grandmother who appears out of thin air.

"Let's have a seat," said Mary, gesturing to one of the round tables Pat remembered sitting at during Sunday school those many years ago. Her life was turning upon itself, it seemed, with all the lost things becoming found and the painful things becoming pleasant. Where would it end?

"I made you a little something," said Pat, as she bent down and reached into her bag. "It's not much, just a few old pictures, but I thought you might like to see what some of your relatives looked like."

Mary smiled. "We must be related, because I made you a little something too." She placed a second photo book on the table. "It's not everything, but these are my favorite pictures. I thought you might like to have them."

Pat and Mary spent the next hour and a half talking about the photos and the people pictured in them, and as they did, the feeling grew that they really did belong to one another in some inexplicable way. Pat's family was, indeed, Mary's family, just as Mary's family had become part of Pat's. And Kyle and Elena and Justin and Nicole were Pat's too.

She only wished Mary's mom was still alive. She would have liked to have met the woman who had been a mother to her daughter. Then again, it was probably better this way. Each woman had gotten to have Mary as their very own. Sharing her would have been an awkward thing.

In time, the rest of the Vohwinkel family arrived to meet their newly discovered relative. If Mary was overwhelmed by meeting them, she didn't show it, though encountering a roomful of Vohwinkels all at once was surely enough to induce anyone to renounce all family ties and run out the back door!

Pat's sister walked up to Pat and Mary and asked, "How's it going?"

"It's like we've known each other all our lives!" answered Pat.

"Well, it wasn't like that for me," said her sister. "Imagine getting a phone call from your new pastor announcing that he is really your long-lost nephew-in-law. And his wife is your niece!"

Mary laughed in turn. "How about waking up to find out that the woman on the pew beside you is your aunt, and her sister is your long-lost mother!"

"It's enough to make you want to crawl back into bed until you wake up," added Pat. But she was right; it did feel like they had all known one another for ages. What was it about family that makes all other social complexities fade away?

Pat looked up and saw her niece Becky talking with Jack. They seemed as comfortable with one another as old friends. Jack Marshall. Old friends. Why, they *were* old friends! That was the reason the name *Jack Marshall* had sounded so familiar—he had been the deacon that had struck her as so out of place at Becky's wedding! Pat had met Jack over twenty years ago. Would wonders ever cease!

chapter 34

P at sat in her sister's recliner looking at the photo book Mary had made for her. It was 2:00 a.m., but Pat felt so full of wonder and love and contentment she couldn't possibly think of sleeping.

She brushed her finger lightly over the first picture in the book. It was of Mary at five months old, on the day her parents had brought her home. Where had she been for the first five months of her life, and why had her first family given her back up for adoption? These were questions neither she nor Mary would probably ever be able to answer. Mary looked unsure in that picture, maybe even a bit frightened. Had her first family mistreated her?

The next few pictures showed her in all the happy poses one expects to see when they look at a baby book: crawling on the carpet, getting into the kitchen cupboards. She didn't look frightened any more. She was smiling, confident, and full of curiosity.

Then Pat stared at the school pictures. She couldn't believe her eyes! But for the addition of color, and a slightly updated fashion, Mary's fourth-grade picture looked identical to pictures of Pat at seven and eight years old.

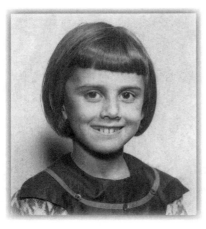

Pat, seven years old.

It was incredible—so like to herself! Visions of her own school years, and their untimely ending, filled her mind, from the brief escape from her father, to her decision to exchange her life as a schoolgirl for one of love and adventure with Harry's father. It was a sad chapter in her life.

Things had been different for Mary, though, and the proof was on the next page. There she was, beautiful and smiling in her senior portrait. She looked radiant. She had made it through

Mary, fourth grade.

246

school, and she was not rough and calloused as she would surely have been if Pat had raised her in the housing project. That was a difficult environment, even for the boys. Pat's heart warmed as she looked at the pictures, for they could not but confirm that she had, indeed, made the right decision when she had released her daughter to be raised in a normal, loving home, with two parents who would care for her and give her all the opportunities a child deserves.

Ah, and there were the grandchildren—Justin and Nicole in one batch, and Kyle and Elena several years later. Pat wondered if she would get to know them at all, and if they would ever get the chance to know her, and to love her like a real grandma. But that was another story. Children's lives are hard enough without

Mary, senior year 1983-1984.

having to contrive an artificial love for a woman they hadn't even known existed! No, she would let the children be. It was enough that she had Mary.

There were other pictures too, of Jack, and of relatives Pat had yet to meet, but her soul was filled, and she did not need to look at those right now. She reached up and turned off the light. Then she held the photo book tightly against her heart and fell asleep.

Christian Light Publications is a nonprofit, conservative Mennonite publishing company providing Christ-centered, Biblical literature including books, Gospel tracts, Sunday school materials, summer Bible school materials, and a full curriculum for Christian day schools and homeschools. Though produced primarily in English, some books, tracts, and school materials are also available in Spanish.

For more information about the ministry of CLP or its publications, or for spiritual help, please contact us at:

Christian Light Publications
P. O. Box 1212
Harrisonburg, VA 22803-1212

Telephone—540-434-0768
Fax—540-433-8896
E-mail—info@clp.org
www.clp.org